WILLIAM BERANEK, JR.
editor

California Institute of Technology

SCIENCE

SCIENTISTS

AND SOCIETY

BOGDEN & QUIGLEY, INC.

PUBLISHERS

TARRYTOWN-ON-HUDSON, NEW YORK

BELMONT, CALIFORNIA

Cover design by Aaron Hirsh

Text design by Science Bookcrafters, Inc.

Library of Congress Catalog Card No.: 72-184807

Standard Book No.: 0-8005-0034-2

Printed in the United States of America

1 2 3 4 5 6 7 8 9 10—76 75 74 73 72

Preface

Today, with science involved in our society as never before, the thoughtful scientist takes time to consider his possible roles in society. He asks, "With my abilities and my personal needs, what can I best do for science? What can I best do for man? How can I best accomplish these goals in my society at this time?"

This is a book of lectures given to stimulate introspection about these questions. The lectures were presented to the division of chemistry and chemical engineering at the California Institute of Technology during the winter quarter, 1971. Although the series—"Chemistry and Society"—was designed primarily for the benefit of chemists at Caltech, it drew a much wider audience—scientists from all divisions of the Institute, students, nonscientists, and many from the off-campus community. This was testimony to the wide interest in the questions discussed and to the distinguished quality of the speakers.

Using the American chemist as an example, Dr. Daniel Kevles, Caltech history of science professor, traced the history of the moral dilemmas of the scientist in society from the nineteenth century. The chairman of our chemistry division, Dr. George Hammond, spoke of how scientists think about science.

Since a scientist can provide insight into areas of research other than his own or can even change the direction of his research, three Caltech professors were invited to describe the scientific aspects of some problems facing society: Dr. Haagen-Smit, professor emeritus of bio-organic chemistry, who played a major role in the discovery and subsequent fight to eliminate smog, told of the history and chemistry of air pollution in Los Angeles; Dr. Norman Brooks, professor of environmental science and civil engineering, talked about strategies for solving environmental problems; and Dr. James J. Morgan, also a professor of environmental engineering, described the distribution of lead and mercury in the environment.

The effect a scientist has, or can have, on society varies with his job. In industry, the scientist works in relative anonymity under the shelter of company secrets. If he is successful, his research will have a direct effect on society. Such a successful scientist, Dr. Maurice Barusch of Standard Oil Company, presented a personal account of the development of the fuel additive F-310.

In academia, a scientist can be successful without considering the direct influence of his research on society. Dr. Max Delbrück, professor of biology at Caltech and Nobel prize winner, thought aloud with us about his life in academic science and his reasons for doing basic research.

Because science today is largely supported by the government and because there is a scientific aspect to many of today's social problems, involvement in political decisions is another important role of a scientist. Dr. Lee DuBridge, former science advisor to President Nixon, sketched the picture of science and politics in the United States from World War I to the present.

The seminar series was concluded with a discussion involving three prominent chemists, Dr. Norman Davidson, Dr. George Hammond, both of Caltech, and Dr. Harry Drickamer of the University of Illinois, on the future of chemistry as a discipline, "How a chemist in today's society best serves science."

The lectures in this book are adapted from tapes of each session. Unfortunately, the discussions following the talks were difficult to record, and we were unable to transcribe several of them.

Through this series, my colleagues and I learned much about ourselves and our profession. I hope this spirit will be reflected on these pages.

I wish to express my appreciation to the men who prepared and delivered these talks and then, despite demands on their time, cooperated so fully with me in preparation of this book. Further, I would like to extend my gratitude to Drs. Fred Anson, William Corcoran, Norman Davidson, Richard Dickerson, Sheldon Friedlander, Harry Gray, Aron Kupperman, Cornelius Pings, and John Roberts, who introduced the speakers and led the discussion sessions; to secretaries in and out of the division whose help was invaluable; and to my friends throughout the division whose enthusiasm and honest criticism helped make this project a success. I would especially like to thank Dr. George Hammond, who was a source of support and encouragement from the beginning.

Pasadena, California   WILLIAM BERANEK, JR.

Acknowledgments

Arie J. Haagen-Smit: *Theory and Practice of Air Conservation*
  Figures 2, 3, 4, and 5: Reprinted by permission of A. R. Barringer, Barringer Research Ltd., Ontario, Canada.
  Figure 9: Reprinted from Project Clean Air Report on Research Project S-20; by permission of James Edinger, UCLA, and the Director, Project Clean Air.

Norman H. Brooks: *Energy and the Environment*
  Entire article adapted from *Engineering and Science,* January 1971. Published at The California Institute of Technology; by permission.

James J. Morgan: *Trace Metals in the Environment*
  Figure 1: Reprinted, with permission, from "Mineral Cycles" by Edward S. Deevey, Jr. Copyright © 1970 by Scientific American, Inc. All rights reserved.
  Figure 2: From *Environmental Science and Technology, 3,* 474 (1969). Copyright © 1969 by the American Chemical Society. Reprinted by permission of the copyright owner.
  Figure 3: From *Environmental Science and Technology, 4,* 56 (1970). Copyright © 1970 by the American Chemical Society. Reprinted by permission of the copyright owner.
  Figure 4: From *Environmental Science and Technology, 4,* 56 (1970). Copyright © 1970 by the American Chemical Society. Reprinted by permission of the copyright owner.
  Figure 5: From *Environmental Science and Technology, 4,* 249 (1970). Copyright © 1970 by the American Chemical Society. Reprinted by permission of the copyright owner.
  Figure 6: Reprinted from *Earth and Planetary Science Letters, 1,* 397–400 (1966); by permission of North-Holland Publishing Company.
  Figure 7: Reprinted from *Advances in Water Pollution Research, 3,* 153–180 (1967); by permission of the Water Pollution Control Federation.
  Figure 8: Reprinted from W. Berg et al., Mercury content of Swedish birds from the past hundred years, *Oikos, 17,* 71–82 (1966); by permission.
  Figure 9: From *Environmental Science and Technology, 4,* 767 (1970).

Copyright © 1970 by the American Chemical Society. Reprinted by permission of the copyright owner.

Figure 10: From *Environmental Science and Technology, 4,* 767 (1970). Copyright © 1970 by the American Chemical Society. Reprinted by permission of the copyright owner.

Figure 11: From Sanuel H. Williston, *Journal of Geophysical Research, 73,* 7055 (1968).

Table 1: From H. J. M. Bowen, *Trace Elements in Biochemistry,* Academic Press, New York, 1966, p. 163; by permission of the publisher.

Table 2: From Norman H. Brooks, Some Data on Municipal Waste Discharges to Pacific Ocean in Los Angeles Area, unpublished report, 1969; by permission.

Table 3: From J. P. Riley and G. Skirro, eds., *Chemical Oceanography,* Academic Press, London and New York, 1965, p. 185; by permission of the publisher.

Table 4: From *Environmental Science and Technology, 4,* 225 (1970). Copyright © 1970 by the American Chemical Society. Reprinted by permission of the copyright owner.

Table 5: From *Environmental Science and Technology, 4,* 225 (1970). Copyright © 1970 by the American Chemical Society. Reprinted by permission of the copyright owner.

Table 6: From *Environmental Science and Technology, 4,* 767 (1970). Copyright © 1970 by the American Chemical Society. Reprinted by permission of the copyright owner.

Maurice R. Barusch: *History of the Development of F-310*
All illustrations courtesy of the Chevron Research Company, Richmond, California.

Max Delbrück: Homo scientificus *according to Beckett*
Quotation on pp. 139–146 from pp. 69–74 of "Molloy" from *Three Novels: Molloy, Malone Dies, The Unnamable.* Reprinted by permission of Grove Press, Inc. Translated from the French by Patrick Bowles in collaboration with the author. Copyright © 1955, 1956, 1958 by Grove Press, Inc. British and Commonwealth rights held by Calder & Boyars Ltd.; reprinted with their permission.
All illustrations drawn by Vivian Hill.

Contents

SCIENCE   SCIENTISTS

AND SOCIETY

DANIEL J. KEVLES

is associate professor of history at Caltech. His field of interest is the social and political history of science in the United States. He was a physics major as an undergraduate at Princeton, studied a year at Oxford University in England, then returned to Princeton, where he received his Ph.D. in history in 1964.

CHAIRMAN
Richard E. Dickerson
Professor of Physical Chemistry
Caltech

DANIEL J. KEVLES

On the Moral Dilemmas
of the American Chemist:
Some Notes from History

DICKERSON: Dr. Kevles did his undergraduate work at Princeton in physics and then went on from there to history for a Ph.D., also at Princeton, in 1964. His particular field, not too surprisingly, is the interaction of science and technology and the cultural history of science and technology. He has agreed to put into historical perspective the underlying theme of this series: "moral dilemmas of the American chemist."

KEVLES: Many contemporary American chemists, especially many younger ones, are torn between what their institutional patrons are alleged to expect of them and what they prefer to expect of themselves. Should they do research supported by the Department of Defense when the military, in the opinion of a sizable fraction of the public, is exerting a deleterious influence over the nation's foreign policy? Should they accept research grants from corporations that aid the military or pollute the environment? For a number of thoughtful scientists, chemists or not, these questions are so acute as to amount to moral dilemmas, and they permit no easy resolution. But we may at least cast some light upon them by exploring their historical background.

In the late nineteenth century, American scientists felt none of these dilemmas, if only because they had few, if any, real institutional patrons. It was, of course, an age of practicality. Most Americans were primarily interested in conquering the West, mining or plowing the earth, and building a powerful industrial nation. And most held the expert, especially the scientific expert, in contempt,

3

even hostility. Farmers produced ever more crops without the aid of soil scientists, steelmakers turned out ever more ingots without the advice of chemists, and Thomas Edison, the symbol of his technological age, seemed to need no physicists to invent and develop a commercially feasible system of electrical lighting. The antiexpert convictions of the industrial establishment found perfect summary in the remark of the trade journal *Electrical World*: "Edison's mathematics would hardly qualify him for admission to a single college or university . . . but we would rather have his opinion on electrical questions than of most physicists" (*Electrical World*, September 20, 1884, p. 96).

The United States did have its scientific, including its chemical, professions, but all of them were small. In 1815, America had an estimated 455 chemists; by 1880, only, at the outside, about 2000. In 1890, there were only about 276 chemists in all of the nation's industry. The vast majority of pure scientists in any discipline were employed in the academic world, primarily in universities, and in the academic world the pure chemist operated under a regime of impoverishment. He had almost no endowments for research; he had few good laboratories (it was said that Edison's research facilities in Menlo Park were far superior to those in any university). Above all, he could expect few if any rewards for achievement in pure science. You rose through the academic hierarchy primarily on the basis of your teaching. If the scientific professions were small, it was not the least because most Americans simply could not afford careers which yielded no material rewards. Pure science was primarily populated by men who either came from upper-middle-class backgrounds or who married upper-middle-class women.

Ignored by their countrymen and populated by the well-to-do, the scientific community in the United States developed an ideology of pure science. Latter-day attempts to define the phrase "pure science" in terms of what it means in practice have usually led to semantic confusion. When someone does applied research, he may stumble upon a valuable contribution to fundamental knowledge. Conversely, when someone does pure research, he may just as likely hit upon a useful item of technology. But in the late nineteenth century, the practitioners of pure science did not define the phrase simply by the nature of the knowledge they were seeking. They also included a motive, and that motive was the pursuit of knowledge without the pursuit of material (meaning economic) gain. To do pure science at that time connoted a kind of nobility and high-mindedness that was quite in contrast to the profit-oriented, corner-cutting, frequently corrupt value system dubbed Grantism. If most Americans were emphasizing a kind of economic and technological nationalism, the advocates of pure science, both lay and professional, agreed with Henry Adams that the only way to measure the progress of a nation was by the progress of its thought.

No one better stated the ideology of pure science, with all its smug connotations, than the Johns Hopkins physicist Henry Rowland. Speaking before the American Association for the Advancement of Science in 1883, Rowland declared: "American science is a thing of the future and not of the present or past. The proper course for one in my position is to consider what must be done to create a science of physics in this country rather than to call telegraphs, electric lights, and such conveniences by the name of science." Rowland did not wish to underrate the value of all these things. "The progress of the world depends on them," he admitted, "and he is to be honored who cultivates them successfully. So also the cook who invents a new and palatable dish for the table benefits the world to a certain degree, yet we do not dignify him by the name of chemist." Rowland's speech won wide applause in the scientific community, and it was called "A Plea for Pure Science" [Henry Rowland, A Plea for Pure Science, *The Physical Papers of Henry Augustus Rowland* (Baltimore: Johns Hopkins University Press, 1902), p. 594].

But even while Rowland was holding forth, changes were occurring in American industry that would eventually bring the nation's scientists into greater rapport with their society. By the turn of the century invention was yielding an ever more complex technology, especially in the chemical and electrical industries. Now industry recognized that it needed the help of scientifically trained engineers and even of scientists themselves. Moreover, industry decided that there was an economic advantage in the patronage of research, even of pure research. New knowledge could lead to new and profitable technology, as General Electric learned from Irving Langmuir's work on the nitrogen lamp. In the early twentieth century industry not only hired college graduates in engineering and science; it also began to create industrial research laboratories.

World War I accelerated the trend. About the turn of the century, when for the first time America's exports exceeded her imports, some industrial leaders had come to realize that, to compete successfully in the international marketplace with such scientifically advanced nations as Germany, industry had to develop a greater scientific capacity. With the advent of World War I, the United States found itself without nitrates from Chile or dyes from

Germany. Cut off from its traditional sources of supply, industry had an even more pressing reason to get into the business of industrial research. As an observer remarked in 1916, "Business has awaked to chemistry as a source of power and wealth as business has never before had occasion or opportunity to be" (James R. Withrow, The American Chemist and the War's Problems, *Science*, June 16, 1916, p. 842).

After the war, the spreading identification of science with the prestige of national economic power helped draw many more young Americans into research than ever before. In 1900, there were an estimated 9000 chemists in the United States; by 1930, an estimated 45,000. The overall growth was reflected in the production of Ph.D.s. Between 1925 and 1934 some 3300 men and women took doctorates in chemistry alone, a dramatically large number compared to the production of Ph.D.s in the late nineteenth century, when the total output in all fields amounted to no more than a few hundred in the average decade. Accompanying the postwar expansion in size was a change in the social composition of the scientific professions. Having become much more an avenue of social and economic mobility —there were now rewards for achievement in pure research—the scientific community drew increasingly from middle-class and even from lower-middle-class families.

The expansion in size combined with the ambitions of the newer practitioners to yield a new kind of scientific leadership. Since many of them were professors, they knew first-hand the need for more academic positions, more research funds, more laboratories. They were a considerably more promotional-minded class of scientists than any of their predecessors, and through the interwar years they made a concerted effort to obtain considerably more money for research, especially pure research.

In the course of appealing for support, they argued for the glories of pure science, but the postwar circumstances made using the economic argument more effective. Industry was investing large sums in research. According to the National Association of Manufacturers, in the 1920s the United States was spending some $200,-000,000 annually on scientific research, and industrial corporations were responsible for a good two thirds of the total, twice as much as the federal government. No discipline received a larger share of the burgeoning industrial patronage than chemistry.

Most of the industrial investment went into industry's own research laboratories. In these establishments, young scientists found ample facilities, good salaries, and, so it was frequently claimed, rich opportunities to pursue the fundamental side of their disciplines. But, in fact, the vast majority of staff in the usual industrial laboratory were not given the freedom to follow their intellectual fancies. That privilege was reserved to a small, elite group, exemplified by Langmuir at General Electric or Clinton Davisson at Bell Laboratories. Most industrial scientists were subject to the direction of the laboratory director, and he chose the research topics primarily on grounds of what was likely to lead to the quickest profits for his company. Budding young scientists eager to explore the key problems on the frontiers of their disciplines found the industrial world relatively unattractive. They preferred to settle down in the world of the universities.

During the interwar years, academic science acquired a good deal more money than it had ever known before, but, for a bevy of legal and institutional reasons, the funds for pure science did not come from corporations. Public universities, of course, were blessed by state legislative appropriations. Private universities received endowments from such wealthy benefactors as George Eastman or the DuPonts and, more important, from the major philanthropic foundations, especially the Rockefeller Foundation and the Carnegie Corporation of New York. In the 1920s, through its various agencies, the Rockefeller Foundation donated some $19,000,000 to science in the private universities. Although by today's standards that sum may seem miniscule, it was an enormous amount of money at the time, especially when measured against the much smaller sums available for university research in the preceding decades.

The scientific community took good advantage of the new money. In the 1920s the physical sciences in the United States came into their own, and, by the beginning of the 1930s, before the flight of the refugees, many observers agreed that the American scientific community was close to being on a par with its counterparts in Europe. The funding that made the rise in stature possible derived to no small extent from the economic argument for pure research and from the response of the economically interested groups that became its patrons.

Coincident with this development, the nation experienced a thrust for military patronage of science, primarily during World War I. Before that war the Army and Navy had operated largely without the aid of scientists. Neither service had any real research laboratories. Like industry, both relied on in-house engineers who were Edisonian in their thinking or outside inventors who were no different. But even before the United States entered the war, it was clear to some military men that submarines, aircraft, and chemical warfare were raising technological challenges that the military establishment was ill prepared to cope with. Although by 1917 neither service had done much to overcome its technical inadequacies, both went to unprecedented lengths to exploit the military capabilities of science during America's participation in the war. Physicists built devices for the detection of submarines, chemists developed new munitions, mathematicians solved problems in ballistics and shell design, and psychologists found a use for their expertise in personnel work by developing the first massive intelligence testing operation in the history of the United States.

The military's embrace of science found exemplary expression in the development of its capacity to wage chemical warfare. When the nation entered the war, the Army did not even have a gas mask in its defensive arsenal, let alone an array of offensive chemical weapons. Moreover, the American chemical industry had not done any preliminary research or development in the field. But the Army, together with various civilian scientific agencies in and out of the government, quickly got a chemical warfare program going, and eventually all the efforts were consolidated under the direction of the new Chemical Warfare Service. By the end of the war the Army had a massive capability in gas warfare. Had the war lasted into 1919, it was estimated that the United States would have been producing more advanced chemical weapons than all the belligerent powers in Europe combined.

At the end of the war, like most other technical bureaus in the Army and Navy, the Chemical Warfare Service argued for a peacetime military research and development program which would heavily involve civilian scientists. But the nation had been shocked by the first gas attack at Ypres in 1915, and it was cool to the idea. More important, the Service faced telling opposition from men at the highest echelons of the Army itself, notably Chief of Staff Peyton C. March. An old professional soldier, March had his professional code of ethics. To his mind, chemical warfare was an unacceptable weapon because it risked the lives of civilians. March's discontent may seem quaint to a generation that has known the destruction of civilians from Guernica to Hiroshima and on to Vietnam. It was real enough to March, and at the end of the war he argued vigorously for the abolition of the Chemical Warfare Service. Secretary of War Newton D. Baker, who felt precisely the same way, abolished the Service by executive action.

General Amos A. Fries, the chief of the Chemical Warfare Service, refused to accept the destruction of his bureau. Following the usual practice of his day, he took his case directly to the Congress, and the issue of the Chemical Warfare Service found dramatic expression in the hearings on the bill for the general reorganization of the Army which were held in 1919 and 1920. Peyton March testified against the continuation of the Service, emphasizing the threat of chemical warfare to the civilian population. But General Fries had an unabashed rebuttal to March's fundamental point. As a weapon that placed noncombatants in jeopardy, Fries said, gas was scarcely unique. Some two hundred people had been killed when the Germans managed to reach Paris with a long-range gun. Hundreds more had died when German bombers attacked French cities and even distant London. (Fries could also have pointed out the thousands who would have certainly met their deaths had the Allies used airplanes to drop one-ton containers of mustard gas on the fortified cities of Metz and Coblentz, an offensive tactic they seriously considered and, had the war continued, might have carried out.) Fries needed no elaboration to make his fundamental counter to March. The issue was not some new form of warfare but the historic one of war itself.

But if you "kept on with these scientific means of destruction," a Senator anxiously wondered, wouldn't you run the danger of "wiping out the whole human race?" [United States Congress, Senate, *Reorganization of the Army*, Hearings before the Subcommittee of the Committee on Military Affairs, 66th Congress, 1st and 2nd Sessions, August 7 to December 7, 1919 (2 volumes; Washington, D.C.: Government Printing Office, 1920), Vol. I, p. 178].

Fries had the ultimate answer. The more "deadly" the weapons, "the sooner . . . we will quit all fighting." If war could be made "so terrible" that it would not last "more than five or ten minutes," then war would never begin (*ibid.*, Vol. I, pp. 364–365).

Fries won his battle. Congress granted the Chemical Warfare Service permanence, and Fries became its peacetime Chief. If in his testimony the General had adumbrated an element of some significance in a later generation's drive to embrace military research and development, in his first annual report he anticipated the argument right down to the code word. America's ever-developing chemical arsenal, Fries said, would go a long way toward "deterring" other countries from even starting wars (Report of the Chief of Chemical Warfare Service, in *United States War Department, Annual Report, 1920*, Vol. I, pp. 1887–1888).

But if the military came out of World War I with a much en-larged technical establishment and with quite modern arguments to justify it, neither the Army nor the Navy managed to sustain a major program of research and development between the wars. With the country quickly retreating into isolationism, military appropria-tions were cut back. They remained so low that one whimsical Con-gressman remarked that the American Army was no longer standing but sitting down. In the middle of it all, the military had little money to fund research, and it was in no position to provide patronage for science outside its own bureaus in the academic or the industrial worlds. All the same, World War I set the precedent for military involvement in the nation's research community, and the precedent would, of course, come to be of prime importance in the years following World War II.

After World War I, the military precedent contributed to the development of a public ambivalence toward science. It was an ambivalence that originated in the extent to which science could be used for destructive purposes, and it was clearly evident in the as-sault against science mounted in the interwar years by many thoughtful spokesmen. Professors, poets, and writers—they called themselves humanists, and they commanded wide public attention.

No thoughtful American could help but respond to the human-ist indictment of technology. If science had helped win the Great War, it would make the next war catastrophic, particularly, as more than one writer worriedly pointed out, were man to discover the secret of atomic energy. Then, there was the dehumanizing effect of the machine: The automobile industry might have created jobs for tens of thousands, but the assembly line had robbed blue-collar workers of the pleasures of craftmanship, and the organization of mass production had turned white-collar employees into faceless cogs in a corporate machine. There was, as Charles Beard summa-rized it, the blight of urban, technological civilization: "New York City from the elevated railway, huge sections of Pittsburgh and Chicago, shabby and dilapidated water fronts, glorious spots of na-ture made hideous by factories, endless rows of monotonous dwell-ings, the shameful disregard of beauty along the highways from Boston to San Francisco, magnificent avenues through forest and valley ruined by billboards and gas-filling shacks, fretful masses rushing from one mechanical show to another, the horrible out-pouring of radio nonsense, natural and canned, the unceasing roar and grind of urban life" [Charles Beard, ed., *Towards Civilization* (New York: Longmans, Green, 1930), p. 11].

Through all the humanist critique one word kept cropping up, and that word was *values*. Some scientists seemed to argue that morality progressed with the progress of research. The humanists replied: Science merely described; it did not speak to timeless questions of right and wrong. Although modern man knew more than Socrates, he was surely neither wiser nor more decent. Whereas industry and even nations could write checks against science, science neither checked the rapacious industrialist nor did it make bellicose nationals any less bellicose. In fact, a number of penetrating critics charged, scientism had so eaten away at traditional values that thoughtful men found themselves burdened with the despair of moral relativism. Where are our great moralists? Henry Seidel Canby wondered. "Our Miltons have gone in for mathematics, biology, and atomic research" (Henry Seidel Canby, Render Therefore Unto Caesar, *Saturday Review of Literature*, May 4, 1929, p. 970).

In the interwar years, the nation's scientific leadership heard the charges of the humanists—and largely brushed them aside. During the debate over the Chemical Warfare Service, General Fries found some of his most prestigious allies in the officers of the American Chemical Society and the editors of various chemical journals. In the more general debate over the course of America's ever more urban, technological civilization, the scientific community's position was exemplified by one of its most famous members, the head of the California Institute of Technology and the 1923 winner of the Nobel prize in physics, Robert A. Millikan.

Millikan perceived the "chief menace" to civilization not in science but in the "emotional, destructive, over-sexed" content of modern literature and art. He scoffed at the anxiety over technology. With high authority, a good deal of support from most physicists, and a special bow to the Creator for building some "fool-proof" safeguards into His handiwork, Millikan assured that the energy locked in the atom was destined to stay there. With something less than sterling logic, he announced that, whatever the problems of urban congestion, or even of gangsters with getaway cars, the automobile had created "a new race" of responsible, abstemious men. Why, just "contrast the clear-eyed, sober, skillful, intelligent-looking taxi driver of today with the red-nosed wreck of a human being who used to be the London cabby of a quarter century ago. . ." [R. A. Millikan, Science and Modern Life, *Atlantic, 141* (April 1928), 490, 495; Millikan, Alleged Sins of Science, *Scribner's Magazine, 87* (February 1930), 121].

Like Millikan, almost no American scientist, certainly no major

American scientist, manifested any sense of moral dilemma over the practice of pure science, on the one hand, and the purposes for which it received financial support, on the other. This is by no means to say that they were not moral men. If they displayed no more moral concern than other men, they certainly showed no less. They were simply not bothered by the issues to which a later generation of scientists would become so sensitive.

Why not? For one thing, they had assimilated the ideology of pure science articulated by their predecessors. No matter how utilitarian the arguments they made to the public, by practicing or administering pure science they could consider themselves disinterested souls who were *ipso facto* high-minded and who, as such, were carrying forward one of the highest tasks of civilization. For another thing, like Millikan, the nation's scientific leaders were not only pure scientists; they were also promoters. Bent upon the expansion of the scientific community and raising money for that purpose, they were in no position to take the humanist indictment seriously. To admit to the faults charged against science was to jeopardize its growth.

The scientific generation that came of age during World War II could not—and did not wish to—brush aside these moral issues so easily. The economic argument for science helped mobilize the Congress to legislate for research, and so, to a much greater extent, did the military rationale. After V-J day, Americans did not retreat into isolationsim, especially since by 1947 they saw the nation in a Cold War with the Soviet Union. The new generation of scientific leaders had no qualms about accepting funds legislated on grounds of military advantage. The amount of federal support, particularly support from the Department of Defense, raised the prestige and funding of academic science to a vastly higher level. Moreover, the nation's scientific leadership, like most other Americans in the postwar decades, considered it emphatically important to maintain the country's military, technological, and, accordingly, scientific strength in the face of the Soviet threat. All the same, many thoughtful Americans felt the same ambivalence toward science as did the humanists between the wars, and in this postwar period those thoughtful Americans included some of the country's leading scientists.

No scientist better symbolized the profession's moral sensitivity than the former director of the laboratory at Los Alamos, J. Robert Oppenheimer. Shortly after the war Oppenheimer confided to President Truman that he felt as though he had blood on his hands. In the later 1940s and through the 1950s, Oppenheimer was also concerned about the ever-larger and more destructive arsenal of nuclear weapons. Burdened by an acute sense of moral responsibility, Oppenheimer frequently articulated to the public the moral dilemmas of his fellow professionals. To many members of the postwar public, particularly to those of a humanist, liberal frame of mind, J. Robert Oppenheimer emerged as a combination of Mr. Science and Mr. Conscience.

In the postwar years, as a result, the public tended to set aside its ambivalence toward science. It was not just that the nation had a Cold War on its hands. It was also that, while worried about the escalating threat of nuclear weapons, it could trust scientists because they were identified with trustworthy men of conscience like Oppenheimer. For a long time after 1945 the scientific community had the best of both worlds. On the one hand, it derived a considerable amount of money from the military establishment. On the other, it was respected for its evident commitment to conscience and morality.

But since the mid-1960s, and with gathering force in more recent years, the United States has known something of a revolt against science. Especially marked in liberal, humanist circles, the revolt has indicted science for its association with seemingly rapacious technology. The dissidents, concerned about the power of the giant American corporation and about corporate desecration of the environment, insist that the United States should no longer do whatever it is capable of doing technologically simply because it is capable of doing it. An exemplary symptom of this side of the revolt is the assault against the supersonic transport. Why fund Boeing? the critics ask. Why subsidize the traveling convenience of business executives? Above all, why risk injury to the environment and raise the already atrocious noise level?

The revolt has found its chief target in the military role of science. Doubtless the discrediting of the military because of Vietnam has had a good deal to do with the attack against the support of science by the Department of Defense. In any case, the revolt has called into serious question the legitimacy, even the morality, of permitting research to be funded by two of its principal postwar patrons, the industrial corporation and the Department of Defense.

It is because the real target of the revolt has been the institutions with which science has become primarily identified that many scientists today, especially many younger scientists, feel a sense of moral dilemma. And it is probably because these younger scientists see the world in a different way from preceding generations that the sense of moral dilemma is so acute. Today's scientists have not had to fight the battle for national recognition of science. Indeed, they have come to professional maturity in an era when science was dominant, respected, and prestigious. Furthermore, as younger scientists, they share to an extent in the values and attitudes of the current youth culture; hostile to our involvement in Vietnam, they regard the so-called military–industrial complex with deep suspicion. Whatever the origins of their discontent, it is genuine—and it has spread to many thoughtful members of the older generation.

But today's scientists, morally sensitive or not, all face a difficult practical problem. Although all are eager to do pure science, they find themselves struggling with a crisis in the funding of research which is itself a product of the revolt against science. Appropriations for research have become so tight not simply because of conservatives in Congress who balk at spending tax money for any purpose; it is also the result of the liberal discontent with the purposes, particularly the military purposes, for which the public support of research has been justified.

Given the need for funds and given their basic agreement with the liberal motivations for the cutbacks, how are the nation's scientists to ease this crisis? The fact of the matter is that in the United States, as a geologist once said, the appeal must be to utility. Arguments for science for its own sake have not, at least in financial terms, ever gotten very far in this country. So, like their predecessors, today's scientists are compelled to find support for their research by appealing to the nation's utilitarian interests.

Combining their moral sensitivities with the need for a utilitarian argument, some scientists have urged the nation to fund pure research for the purposes of social reform. New knowledge, it is said, will ultimately lead to such social benefits as the elimination of pollution or better public-transportation systems or better sewage disposal. But whatever the extent to which the larger society is interested in solving social problems, in the past its members have rarely considered investing in pure science as the way to gain this end, and they are unlikely to do so now. Society is eager for social solutions today, not tomorrow, and the social payoff from pure research usually lies in the distant future.

Other scientists call for the public to support socially relevant research programs of an applied nature. But for many younger scientists, the ideology of pure science creates a difficult choice. Within the scientific community, prestige tends to be associated a good deal more with achievements in pure rather than in applied science. Nowadays, pure science mainly means attacking those key intellectual problems which lie at the frontier of a given discipline. Applied science of a socially relevant nature means exploring what are often intellectually mundane matters (one need only compare the intellectual challenges of particle physics with those of sewage disposal). In short, the scientific community itself exerts considerable internal pressure to discourage the socially purposeful young away from devoting their lives to socially purposeful research.

How shall the younger scientists resolve these dilemmas? How shall they pursue pure science when they dislike doing it under the patronage of industrially or militarily oriented institutions? How shall they pursue pure science when it is unlikely that they can get funding on the grounds that someday it may serve a good social purpose? How shall they make their way in the scientific community itself if, by doing socially purposeful research, they must quite likely forego that community's greatest respect and rewards?

There are no easy answers to these questions, but one may pose a few suggestions. One obvious possibility is that the morally purposeful younger scientist should simply commit himself to a life of socially purposeful applied research. He must remember that he will not likely win the Nobel prize and that he may suffer the silent disdain of the pure science community. But to ease his way, the older scientists might attempt to restructure the value system which makes it so difficult to leave pure science for applied science. By preaching and example, even by promoting institutional change, they might make careers in socially purposeful applied research considerably more respectable and desirable than they are made to appear now.

Another possibility is for the younger scientists simply to be pure scientists, taking their financial support where it can be found, which means from militarily or industrially interested agencies. Critics may say today that it is somehow immoral to accept research funds from the Department of Defense, but similar claims have been made before in the history of American scholarship. In the interwar years it was charged that to accept research funds from the Rockefeller or Carnegie philanthropies was to accept tainted money. It does not seem that the younger scientists of that day, many of whom were the beneficiaries of these philanthropies, were corrupted by virtue of having worked under a Rockefeller or Carnegie grant or fellowship. In short, it is unlikely that accepting money from the military for pure, unclassified research leads, in pragmatic terms, to an immoral result.

In fact, it could quite possibly lead to the kind of moral result that the dissidents aim to achieve. Today's military undoubtedly contains its Peyton Marches, those who are no less unhappy with the course of American foreign policy—and with the role of the military in shaping that policy—than the morally sensitive scientist. The members of the American scientific community, as well as of many other dissident groups, might well develop a more discriminating view of the military–industrial complex. They might seek among its inhabitants those men who dislike what the phrase stands for in its worst connotations and join with them in an effort to assure that the results of scientific research are not used for immoral ends. To refuse to work with military personnel simply because they are military personnel as such flatly and disadvantageously closes the door to such a strategy.

Above all, young scientists ought to think twice before going so far as to leave science, as some have actually done, because it may seem difficult to reconcile their moral convictions with the practice of research. Science will not stop progressing, even though, at times, some of the critics sound as though they would like it to. In an earlier day it was in fact urged that the United States impose a moratorium on research to give the nation time to learn how to cope with its onrushing technology. The idea was both "impossible and foolish," as Millikan sensibly said (impose a moratorium on science, a more topically minded commentator remarked, and you would get "bootleg science as well as bootleg whiskey") [R. A. Millikan, Science and Modern Life, *Atlantic, 141* (April 1928), 491; A. W. Meyer, That Scientific Holiday, *Scientific Monthly, 27* (December 1928), 542]. The idea was—and is—also counterproductive. The advance of science has, after all, led to considerable advantages for civilization by helping to ease the burden of labor, improve the public health, and raise the standard of living. The world has clearly needed its pure scientists, and there is no doubt that to make a better society it will continue to need them.

At the same time, the nation's current scientific leadership might do well to divest itself of the endless-growth psychology of its predecessors, to step back from the traditional call for an exponential expansion of the scientific professions and research budgets. Clearly this rate of growth cannot continue forever; otherwise, in not too many decades the entire population of the earth would consist of scientists. The *extensio ad absurdum* aside, it *should* not go on forever. There are just too many other needs to be met out of the federal budget. In any case, by accepting a less costly growth rate, the nation's current scientific leadership might help in a round-about way to ease the moral dilemmas of the younger generation simply because in a more equitable society they would not be so acute.

Whatever the specific course of the young or the old, we shall all be the better for it if today's morally sensitive scientists seek to resolve their dilemmas in full recognition of the realities of American life, especially the inevitable tension under which they must operate in a utilitarian society. If they do so, perhaps they will find a way to live not only in greater but also in more effective rapport with their own consciences.

GEORGE S. HAMMOND

is chairman of the Division of Chemistry and Chemical Engineering at Caltech. As Arthur Amos Noyes Professor of Chemistry, his major research interest is photochemistry and chemical dynamics. A graduate of Bates College in Maine, he holds master's and doctor's degrees from Harvard University (1947). After a postdoctoral year at UCLA, he joined the faculty at Iowa State University. He came to Caltech in 1958. He is a member of the National Academy of Science.

CHAIRMAN
Harry D. Gray
Professor of Inorganic Chemistry
Caltech

GEORGE S. HAMMOND

John Chemist
Contemplates his Navel

GRAY: Today's speaker is my sidekick, junior partner, my head PR man. It's a great pleasure to introduce the chairman of the Division, Professor George S. Hammond, to speak to us on the topic "John Chemist Contemplates his Navel."

HAMMOND: I understand that there has been some concern implied by the management of this series because of the possible lack of dignity conveyed by the title of my seminar. I'd like to lend you some real reassurance on that score—I was raised from early childhood with a profound respect for dignity. It may not be quite as important as motherhood to our way of life, but it surely belongs in that value category somewhere. If we were to observe the disappearance of dignity from the American scene I would consider it to be really mandatory to take some very dignified Americans—like Jack Roberts—and place them on reservations where they could propagate under protection so that the species, like the American bison, could be preserved.

This seminar series has, I think, been fascinating, and the Division owes a real vote of thanks to Bill Beranek for the insight and diligence that led him to organize it. For the most part we have been and will continue to look at the chemical components in matters that are considered to be some of society's greatest problems, and I think this as an overall objective is exactly what we should be doing. But I intend to do something else, and that is to look at chemists themselves, since *they* have to be the principal agents in any strategy for improvement of the condition of man through the application of chemical science. We can't do it without them. We might as well try to understand them. I am irritated by strategic

19

planning that people make about societal change and societal development, which frequently seems to be built upon the premise that the human agents are going to be *theoretical* rather than *real* people. Since we seem to be fresh out of theoretical people, I think it behooves us to consider the reality of the people involved.

In his seminar last week, Dan Kevles laid a very good foundation for what I have to say by tracing the recent history of the social context in which chemical science has existed and grown in this country. And this is important because there's no way that we can escape from the fact that where we are now has to be strongly correlated with where we just came from. In addition to our social history, we have a lot of other kinds of histories which influence where we are now, such as functional and philosophical. They all helped produce us as we are. I don't want to go into these histories in significant detail, but only want to note their existence in passing because they are also related in some ways to what I have to say. I was at one time enormously interested in history, and I still think it's interesting, but at the present time I find that my principal preoccupation is with what's here now or likely to turn out in the very near future.

One of the most interesting books that I have ever read is a small volume by Thomas Kuhn called *The Structure of Scientific Revolutions*, which I know many of you are familiar with. If you're not, I recommend it to you strongly. This is a book I had to like because I found in it ideas very similar to some I had been incubating, expressed rather more clearly than I had been able to do. I also found a bunch of other ideas that were sufficiently congenial to convince me that they were about to occur to me anyway. Kuhn's central thesis is that there is in existence a powerful set of paradigms that have an almost overwhelming influence on the way in which science is done. Paradigms are those concepts which are nearly universally accepted as general truth. A scientific revolution, according to Kuhn, occurs when a paradigm, such as the phlogiston theory, undergoes change. Such change is always fraught with enormous trauma because scientists offer tremendous resistance to change of concepts that have been regarded, and used, as the very basis of their scientific thinking. I consider this very natural and something that has to be understood.

Although the concept of paradigm change is very easy to illustrate by looking back, the historical view does not provide any real empathy for the trauma that's involved in the change. I'm afraid this is something that has to be experienced over and over again. It is very easy for us to feel patronizing about the childish attachment of chemists of 150 years ago to the paradigm of "vital force" which was supposed to pervade all organic compounds, differentiating them from inorganic compounds. And yet this notion was held by nearly all respectable chemists of that time. Then, in 1828 Friedrich Wöhler observed the formation of urea directly from ammonium cyanate—the formation of an organic compound from an inorganic compound. Now we look back on this as the death blow to the "vital force" theory. The chemists at that time, however, thought very carefully about this observation and came on the fact that the ammonium cyanate had come from the calcination of animal bones. This was a possible out. And they took that out very simply because the paradigm was so exceedingly important to them in their thinking.

Now I guess that the only way in which we can imagine the pain involved in the change is to think of what some of our own reactions would be to the suggestion that we give up some of our current paradigms. We have a very large number, some of which are enormously vital to us. For example, the idea that matter contains discrete entities which we call molecules and that the molecules contain bonds is a paradigm that I am not about to relinquish. That's the way it is. Now, why am I not? It's simply because this paradigm idea is fundamental—it's been fed into every concrete thought that I have ever had about chemistry, so I think it's quite clear that the decision to relinquish this paradigm would be an enormously painful thing. You see, I know damn good and well that the concept of a molecule containing bonded atoms is a man-made mental construct—that's where it came from, the mind of man. But, emotionally, I *believe* that concept with a rigidity that is virtually unshakable in me and probably in most of you. If so, I think we are on a common ground in recognizing that our paradigms are precious and really worthy of defense.

Neither Kuhn nor I wants to denigrate the men called scientists because of the paradigmatic basis of science. Without paradigms science would have no continuity and would probably be a complete nothing. In fact, I speculate that development of science in the Western world may be related to the fact that Western culture has been uniquely characterized by acceptance of rigid and very definitive paradigms. I don't know whether or not modern science could only arise in a culture that also produced the concept of a single deity, but it occurs to me as a possibility. In any event, I like and respect science, so I must accept and cultivate paradigmatic thinking.

At the same time, I have to recognize that my paradigms, the things I work with and which I basically believe in, are not eternal. Changes in paradigms that will occur after my life make me a little sad because these changes will contribute to the mortality of my own thoughts, but that is not a severe problem. The thought that some scientific paradigm change is occurring right now is *very* disquieting. I just can't tell which of my bagful of small paradigms is going to change. It blows my mind to realize that some of them must change and probably some that I find very precious are going to change. I sometimes guess about where changes are going to occur, but even this is not a very comforting operation. The cold fact of the matter is that some of my guesses are of such a threatening nature that I don't even dare to share them with fellow chemists for fear of being labeled insane. I mean this quite seriously. I have no intention of making a confessional of my most insane thoughts today, so don't press me on that subject. But there is one that I am very serious about and have discussed before. That is the notion that the development of methods for studying complicated systems, making systems science, including chemical science, developing a systems science appropriate for chemical science, is going to become big. And this goes against the grain of a chemical scientific paradigm which says not to touch something if it's big and complicated and doesn't in some way exclusively relate to first principles.

However, I really have experienced some very strong reactions to even very trivial suggestions for paradigm change. A few years ago, for example, I suggested that division of chemistry into the established subdisciplines—organic, inorganic, physical, and analytical, etc.—did not make a lot of sense, and that some alternative substructuring might be more useful for doing and teaching chemical science. When you stop and think about it, this is about as tame a suggestion as one can make for changing a scientific paradigm. Yet, to many chemists the notion was absolutely intolerable —there's no question about it. When we think of change in science, therefore, we must recognize, at least on the emotional level, that a good many people believe that it just cannot happen—they disbelieve in the possibility of real change. I am sure that there are some chemists who really feel that when the sun blows up and the earth is consumed in some kind of nuclear flames, there are going to be organic chemistry textbooks in that bonfire. You stop and think whether or not this is true.

The danger in vocalizing all those questions about scientific values has been brought home to me very clearly. Last spring, when

I was contemplating going to Washington, one of my colleagues told me that I would not be suitable for the job because I am too strongly antiscience in my thinking. And then, because I have spoken several times recently about current problems in science, I get continuous feedback of the impression that I am hopelessly pessimistic. This is not true. I believe that science will survive and that, despite our trauma, our paradigms will change as they have before. Kuhn describes some of the uneasy periods in science which have preceded paradigm change. I believe that it's possible that this correlates with some of the scientific uneasiness that we experience at the present time. The experience is not pleasant, but I think the situation is one that should make us basically hopeful rather than pessimistic.

Science is paradigmatic and scientists, however varied they may be in other ways, have in common the capability of accepting and working with paradigms. This is an asset, a characteristic which I think has to be taken strongly into account when we talk about how science is going to serve the society or, in fact, function at all. I frequently hear suggestions which boil down to the pious notion that all we have to do is to decide where things ought to go, speak to the scientists a little bit, get them to shape up and think right in order to make the whole scene sparkle. This is, of course, nonsense. A program that in any way involves a change in paradigms of science can't possibly work. If all the paradigms are thrown out, there will be no science left, so you have to be careful in what you're asking to be rejected. Changes in style and outlook that require even tolerable paradigm change, even though it may seem pretty minor, may occur so slowly as to frustrate the spectators.

It would really be mind shattering if I thought that chemists and their fellow scientists were alone in this problem. But this is very clearly not the case, and I am very interested to learn that some of the social scientists on this campus regard social-paradigm change as a principal problem of our time. I won't document it extensively, but as a good example there are those who believe that use of GNP growth as an index of national health is an archaic paradigm for this country. But there are others, both economists and politicians, who consider a change in that paradigm to be almost inconceivable, just as inconceivable as we consider changes in some of the scientific paradigms with which we work. A balanced view of the current economic situation is that if we recognize the concomitant problems, and if change really is necessary, GNP growth *will* disappear as a national goal someway or other. This notion placates almost no one, because those who are willing to accept change are uneasy about it, want to get the trauma finished and get it over with, and those who do not accept this change as desirable or inevitable are simply made uncomfortable by the notion that it will happen anyway, if it will, because of the thought that the paradigm may change and leave them with no base of operation. The situation is fundamentally no different from that found in science. However, it's worth noting that a scientist finds it a hell of a lot easier to contemplate a change in an economist's paradigms than in his own, and vice versa. I've gotten a good many directions about change in scientific paradigms from my friendly economist. One consequence of this is that we may be in real danger of creating a society in which everyone looks around and spends his time wondering why all those other silly asses don't change their silly paradigms.

I believe that chemists are now in a particularly painful position—we have problems in common with everyone else and yet I think perhaps our problems are, summed up, more painful and troublesome than those of many others. This is because we are directly involved in so many kinds of paradigm change. I have often stressed the need for changes within our science and talked about things such as disciplinary restructuring and increasing emphasis on what I call the synthetic mode of science. In all justice, I think that grappling with suggestions for change in the scientific paradigms themselves is really all that should be asked of any group of dedicated people. Unfortunately, we cannot stop there. Changing social paradigms have important and direct effects on chemistry, as was clearly indicated by Dan Kevles' lecture last week. He told you that the development of chemistry in this country has, in fact, been very strongly tied to economic development and to the belief that war is an inevitable part of human existence. Both are kinds of paradigms touching the society as a whole that we can see wavering. I think a lot of people who say that chemists have been either immoral or amoral in thinking about the consequences of their work miss an important point. Social paradigms have changed, and to abuse chemists because they did not anticipate those changes is utterly senseless and just plain cruel. The fact of the matter is that these changes were not foreseen. I know how this works from my personal experience. For a year or so during World War II, I made compounds for testing as insect repellants. This was not a thrilling chemical experience. However, I did feel good about it because it seemed like a helpful thing to be doing. I doubt very much that I could react in the same way to the same thing at this time, not because my morality has changed in an enormous way, but simply because the entire significance of having American troops in the tropical countries has changed—there's been an external change.

There are similar dilemmas, large and small, arising from social change. For example, there was a time only a few years ago when chemists in general felt some pride that chemical manipulations had produced DDT. This, of course, has changed. Even at the present time, however, the paradigm balance is such that Indian chemists feel very differently than Americans about DDT, since the use of DDT is believed to have saved hundreds of thousands of Indians from starvation. Their social paradigm is different and so the reaction of their chemists is of course different.

An area in which senior chemists in the country are now absorbing much abuse is the chemical job market. Collapse of this job market is in part related to what I think is an almost unconscious national experiment in groping around, trying an approach to zero economic growth. Those of us who are supposed to be leaders in the field absorb a lot of gas at the present time because this economic phenomenon was not anticipated. This isn't a very rational position. Zero economic growth seems to be inevitable sometime. It just takes simple arithmetic to come to this conclusion, and this has been true for a long time. It was loudly anticipated by Malthus 150 years ago. The problems arise because although we may be able to anticipate that a change will occur, it's damn near impossible to tell when it *will* occur. Although a change was predicted 150 years ago, I don't really think it's kind to say that somebody should have known five years ago that in 1970 it would be here. There is no way in which we can tell even now whether or not the changes that we see at the present time—the slump in chemical, technological economics—is a part of a definitive paradigm change, or simply a part of the precondition—the prechange condition—which, as I say, has been going on for 150 years. Informed and thoughtful people within the chemical industry differ enormously in their guesses on this matter. They differ not because they are stupid, but because they are speculating about a change that cannot be accurately located on a historical time scale until after the fact. A few hundred years from now it may appear to historians that economic paradigms changed very smoothly and that there was only an insignificant hesitation between Malthus and the early twenty-first century. However, when the hesitation covers the life span of several generations, the people in those generations derive damned little comfort from the prospect that ultimately history will iron it all out.

I draw two conclusions from these considerations. First, chemical science is caught in a maelstrom of paradigm change, within the science and because of the things very closely attached to it where change is either going on or about to occur; therefore, this is no place for people who have a low tolerance for ambiguity. I'd say that the first prerequisite for moderately comfortable survival in chemical science at this time and in the near future is going to be the ability to live with ambiguity and a lack of definitive answers. The second conclusion I have come to is that the trauma of paradigm change will surely be great and that our survival as chemists and as people with any degree of personal happiness at all is likely to depend a great deal on mustering some reasonable compassion for ourselves and each other. At times I have been as prone as anyone to label others, both in and out of science, as either crazy or immoral. In the future I shall continue to disagree with people when I disagree with their rates of changing things, but I hope that I can carry out a plan to use fewer inflammatory adjectives when doing so.

ARIE J. HAAGEN-SMIT

is Professor Emeritus of bio-organic chemistry at Caltech. A natural-products chemist, he received his university training at the University of Utrecht in the Netherlands, being awarded his Ph.D. in 1929. He worked on plant hormones for six years before coming to the United States, where his work on essential oils and their odors at Caltech in the 1940s prepared him for his famous analysis of the post-World War II Los Angeles smog. In addition to doing much critical research on smog, he played active and important roles in informing the nonscientific community of the causes of smog at the city, county, state, and federal levels of government. He is a member of the National Academy of Sciences.

CHAIRMAN
Sheldon K. Friedlander
*Professor of Chemical Engineering
and Environmental Health
Caltech*

ARIE J. HAAGEN-SMIT

Theory and Practice of Air Conservation

FRIEDLANDER: It gives me great pleasure to introduce this afternoon's speaker at the Chemistry and Society Seminar, Dr. Arie Haagen-Smit. Dr. Haagen-Smit is world-renowned for his work in the field of air pollution, as well as in other fields, and in particular for his discovery and identification of the source of photochemical smog. In fact, for the recognition of his work he was awarded the Hodgkins Medal by the Smithsonian Institute in 1969. He is also the chairman of the State Air Resources Board. He just informed me that is a nonpaying position, so, tragically, he may be forced to pawn his Hodgkins Medal to support his work for the Air Resources Board. In addition, he has been chairman of the President's task force on air pollution and a host of other committees and organizations associated with air pollution. Today he's going to talk about the theory and practice of air conservation.

HAAGEN-SMIT: Thank you, Sheldon. This smog-fighting business, serving our great State and its Governor, has not exactly increased my bank account. What has increased, though, is my mail. It is surprising how many thoughtful people want to help and advise me. Recently the City of Pasadena failed in procuring natural gas or low-sulfur oil for use in their electric power generating plant, and so I sent some caustic remarks to the newspaper about their readiness to burn high-sulfur oil. This hit a sensitive spot in City Hall. Just this morning I received a letter signed "Mrs. So-and-So" (an old lady in tennis shoes). She wrote: "Dr. Haagen-Smit, why don't you stop writing about smog and do something about it for a change? Since the City Council always sees that Caltech gets everything that they want from the City Council anyhow, it is about time for Caltech to do something in return."

But even my office is not a safe retreat from the smog turbulence. Often I find on my desk notes and clippings from newspapers showing the deep concern for the standard of my mental state. A recent one said: "If the tangled problem of environmental pollution is ever to be overcome, the right people must talk about the right things, with the right information, at the right time and the right place." And so with this almost perfect fit, I feel confident that we will have a fruitful discussion today. The organizer of this seminar kindly suggested that I discuss various aspects of air pollution, beginning with its history in Los Angeles, followed by a discussion of what smog is and what can be done about it.

Looking back, it seemed more or less ordained that someday I would be drawn into the dirty, smelly project of smog research. I think the alchemist Africanus said: "Chemists are a most stupid set of men who contaminate themselves with sulfur and other horrible stinks." And there I was smelling the intriguing vapors of a new, never-described, never-experienced concoction.

I had just finished the isolation and identification of the odors of the pineapple when I opened the window and smelled what we now call "smog." I passed the smoggy air through the cold traps that had served me faithfully in collecting the vapors of the fruits. Three hundred cubic feet of air (equal to the amount of air we breath every day) went through the traps, resulting in a glass filled with an evil-smelling water. I analyzed this "bouquet" of smog and found many organic and nonorganic compounds. In addition, I found a strong oxidizing action, in contrast to the reducing of sulfur dioxide prevalent in the air of eastern cities.

This oxidizing atmosphere reminded me of my student days, when I was determining the structure of some sesquiterpenes ($C_{15}H_{24}$) present in essential oils. To find the position of the double bond, we would ozonize the compound and break it down into acids, aldehydes, and ketones. And here (after a quarter of a century) I was reminded of my experiments which permeated the organic laboratory with ozone and bleached the ornamental plants in the office of my major professor.

The dirty glass of water made a deep impression on me. It was a glass of water that anyone would refuse to drink. Yet we inhale it each day, and the lungs are far more efficient in assimilating all the impurities. I still believe that this glass of water should have found a place in the Smithsonian as a warning to everybody to be careful about what you breathe. This exciting experience directed my thoughts in a completely new direction. I wanted to know more about the nature of the stuff I had collected, where it came from, and what happened to it.

Some twenty years ago the County Air Pollution Control District, an organization created by State law, catalogued some of the chemicals in the air: gasses such as carbon monoxide, sulfur dioxide, and nitrogen oxides, and particulate matter in the form of metal oxides from steel factories and foundries, mineral dust from cement factories, and oil and soot from combustion processes. These pollutants are still the major cause of complaints across the country, but the organics found in the glass of condensed smog accounted for the eye-irritating smogs in the metropolitan area. Los Angeles was the first to note this new phenomenon in air pollution. A cloud of eye irritation moved across the land, starting in the morning and spreading slowly to the east and the north, pushing its way into the valleys of San Gabriel and San Fernando. Telephone calls to the pollution headquarters signaled the progress of the cloud. Its slow movement, covering everything with its grayish formless haze, resembled a plasmodium (Figure 1).

Meteorologists tell us that one reason that Los Angeles got itself into this trouble was its peculiar geographic and meteorological conditions. The ventilation in the Los Angeles region is inadequate to carry away the pollutants. The sea wind during the daytime pushes the effluents of human activity inland, passing over Pasadena into the San Gabriel Valley. But the mountain ranges in the north and east halt their movement. The land wind during the night drives the air back over Pasadena but it is not strong enough to move the pollutants out to sea. As a result, they stagnate and the

Figure 1

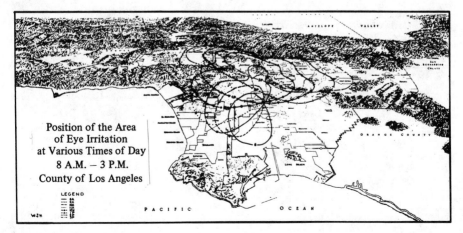

Position of the Area
of Eye Irritation
at Various Times of Day
8 A.M. – 3 P.M.
County of Los Angeles

next morning they are picked up with the new batch of pollutants.

A second reason for the poor ventilation of the Los Angeles region is the almost daily temperature-inversion condition. The temperature at ground level is colder than at higher altitudes. The colder, and therefore heavier, air does not rise and mix freely with the higher layers of the atmosphere. When we consider our basin as a box partially covered by a lid, the height of the box, and therefore the volume, varies with the height of the inversions. When the height doubles, the volume in which the pollutants are dispersed becomes larger and, consequently, their concentration drops. Conversely, when the lid drops, the concentration increases. We can be sure that when the level is lower than 1000 feet, there will be numerous complaints about smog. We have learned to speak about the capacity of the area to accommodate pollutants.

Source measurements have given us information about the quantity of pollutants released in this basin (or airshed, as it is sometimes called). For example, the amount of carbon monoxide released to the air is 14,000 tons per day. This results in concentrations of 20 to 30 parts per million during an average smoggy day. From this you can calculate that the dispersal volume is in the order of 3×10^{11} cubic meters, or corresponding to the volume of a flat box 20 by 20 miles in area 1000 feet high. This corresponds roughly with the volume that we calculate by measuring the basin surface area and multiplying it by the inversion height. Once we know this critical volume it is easy to calculate what concentrations are reached when released in the area. Such calculations served well in the early stages of the studies. At that time, chlorine and sulfur dioxide were suspected as being responsible for the eye-irritating effects and

Table 1

Weight in Tons to Cause Irritation in 625 Square Miles (Inversion base, 1000 ft; volume of air, 500,000,000,000 m³; weight, 650,000,000 tons)

	Smell	Irritation	Tears	Lethal in 10 minutes
Ethyl mercaptan	0.02 (20 kg)			
Synthetic musk	0.005 (5 kg)			
Skatol	0.0002 (0.2 kg)			
Acrolein		80	3,500	180,000
Formaldehyde		–	400	–
Chloroacetophenone		–	150	400,000
Chlorine		185	–	3,000,000
Lewisite		–	400	60,000
Sulfur dioxide		–	30,000	3,000,000

bleach odor noticed during smog attacks. A simple calculation (as shown in Table 1) shows you that you can forget about such an idea. You need to release nearly 200 tons of chlorine and some 30,000 tons of sulfur dioxide before reaching irritation levels. You just don't loose such quantities by accident. Even highly toxic gases, such as the poisonous gas lewisite, require the release of hundred of tons.

For odors, however, far less material is necessary to cause widespread complaints. Table 2 shows that you need only 20 kilograms of ethyl mercaptan to perfume the whole basin. But a chemist can do much better. Because of my past interest in flavors, I often had the opportunity to brighten up the atmosphere in the biology lab. I remember once we got rid of a few grams of sweet-smelling fractions of onion concentrate. Within minutes we got excited calls from the nerve physiologists three floors up. Now if you want to smell up the whole basin, you need add only 5 kilograms of synthetic musk to the attractions of Los Angeles. If you choose skatol, the odorous component of feces, and if you smuggled only a ½ pound up the tower of City Hall, your fame would spread through the air from Santa Monica to Palm Springs.

Odor is an important part of the total pollution problem. Meat-rendering plants sometimes spread an unbearable stench for several miles. Refineries can readily be recognized by their odor. Much effort has gone into the control of such sources, but the problem is still not licked. The difficulty lies in the extreme sensitivity of our sense of smell. I remember that once I woke up in the middle of the night from a peculiar odor. It was not the skunk mercaptan, secondary-butyl mercaptan, but it reminded me more of a petroleum mercaptan. Soon telephone calls flooded the switchboard at the Los Angeles County Air Pollution District office. Marking the positions of the calls on a map gave an ellipse-like curve. This pinpointed the

Table 2
1969 Emissions in Tons per Day in the South Coastal Basin

	Combustion sources		Noncombustion sources: industry and solvents
	Agricultural, burning, power plants, incineration	Automobiles, airplanes, etc.	
Hydrocarbons	1,000	2,500	850
Particulate matter	150	130	50
Oxides of nitrogen	400	1,000	30
Sulfur dioxide	400	60	60
Carbon monoxide	200	14,000	30

culprit—a refinery. It happened that an employee had been bothered for some time by a barrel with unknown contents. By turning it over in a ditch, he made a classical contribution to the study of turbulent diffusion of pollutants.

So we knew at the beginning that whatever the chemical was that was causing eye irritation, it was being released in huge quantities. This led us initially to suspect combustion processes. When emissions inventories finally became available, combustion sources ranked at the top (Table 2).

There are, of course, other sources, and these are well catalogued by the control authorities. Their testing crews in the field determine emissions, in concentrations mostly in the order of a few hundred to a few thousand parts per million. The county station for the west San Gabriel Valley is on our campus. It records sulfur dioxide, hydrocarbons, ozone, oxides of nitrogen, and particulate matter. On the basis of the analytical values, alerts are called that are meant to discourage certain industrial activities and unnecessary driving. Until now the system of alerts has served to keep the pollution problem before the people. Many people ask what they are supposed to do when alerted. The answer is quite simple: You just become alert, that is all.

Tremendous progress has been made in the field of analytical chemistry since I analyzed Los Angeles smog some twenty years ago. I do not want to give you a review of the various methods, but I will single out a recent development that illustrates the extent to which modern methods are able to make undreamed-of progress in plot-

Figure 2

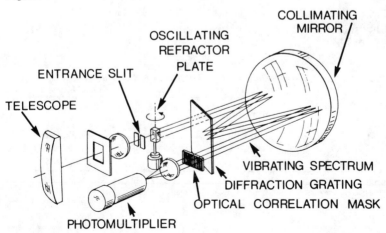

Figure 3

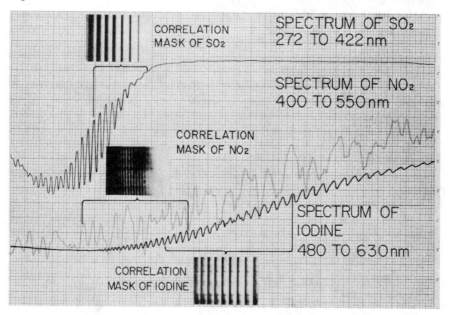

Figure 4

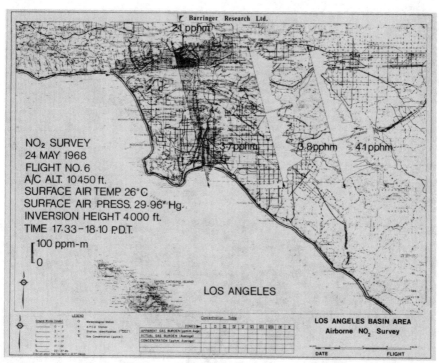

ting the distribution of pollutants over the country.

The instrument in Figure 2 is called a correlation spectroscope. It compares a known absorption spectrum, for example that of iodine, with that of an unknown spectrum. Iodine has quite a characteristic banded spectrum, and by oscillating this over the unknown, a beat signal is produced, its strength related to the degree of correlation. This instrument was developed largely to detect oil fields. It

Figure 5

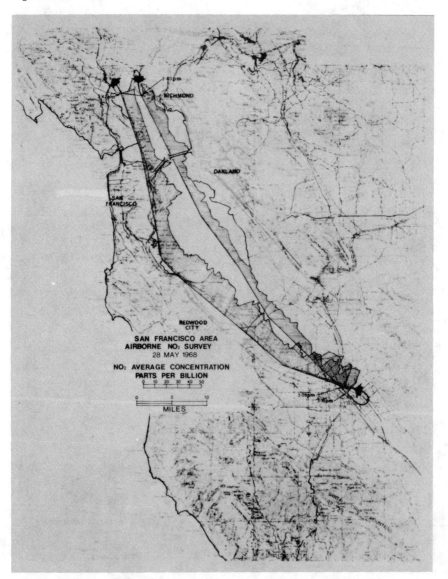

SAN FRANCISCO AREA
AIRBORNE NO₂ SURVEY
28 MAY 1968

NO₂ AVERAGE CONCENTRATION
PARTS PER BILLION

MILES

is so sensitive that kelp beds can be detected by means of their iodine content just by flying over the waters off the coast. The Barringer Corporation, who developed this instrument, has made several flights over Los Angeles, and Figure 3 shows you the result of a nitrogen dioxide survey from a 3000-foot altitude. In this case the comparison filter was, of course, that of NO_2. In Figure 4 you see the peak of NO_2 from the 13 stacks of power plants in the Long Beach area. North of these you see the peaks produced by other industry and finally the massive production over downtown Los Angeles by hundreds of thousands of automobiles. Figure 5 shows a flight between San Jose and Richmond. Of particular interest is the peak near the entrance of the Bay Bridge where people pay their quarters. The traffic congestion at the entrance is faithfully recorded by the increase in the oxides of nitrogen. One step further and with a little more accuracy we might even count the cars or spot exceptionally bad engines by exhaust analysis. These developments are no longer a dream. Considerable progress is being made in the distant recording of industrial emissions.

Oxidants, largely ozone, were found to be an important symptom typical of the Los Angeles smog. They are measured by their ability to oxidize potassium iodide to free iodine. They are formed as soon as the sun rises, reach a maximum in Pasadena during the middle of the day, and disappear when the sun goes down. With the aid of the monitoring system and meteorological data, it is possible to make horizontal plots of the distribution of these oxidants (Figure 6). Figures 7 and 8 give a contour map of the levels over Los Angeles.

Dr. Edinger, a meteorologist from UCLA, has added another

Figure 6

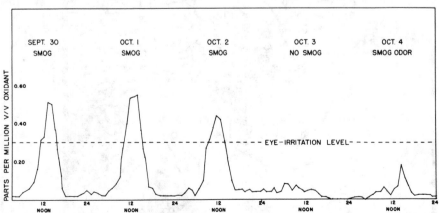

dimension to this picture. He took an oxidant meter with him in a plane and probed the chemical composition of the atmosphere at various altitudes beginning at Santa Monica and ending up in San Bernardino. It takes considerable coordination to even attempt such flights, but the results certainly justify the effort.

Figure 9 shows the gradual formation of the oxidants in the course of the day. Notice that the inversion layer follows more or less the terrain and that the initial formation of the oxidants takes place under this layer. (An interesting phenomenon is seen at the east side near the San Bernardino Mountains, where the pollutants manage to escape above the layer and are apparently captured by a westerly wind driving them out to sea.) Evidently near the mountains there is so much turbulence that the sharp division between the cold and warm layers disappears. The first trip was at 9:30 in the morning. The oxidant level was quite low and the inversion height about 1500 feet. The next flight was at 1:20 P.M. The concentration

Figure 7

Areal Distribution of Oxidant, Los Angeles Basin, November 1955

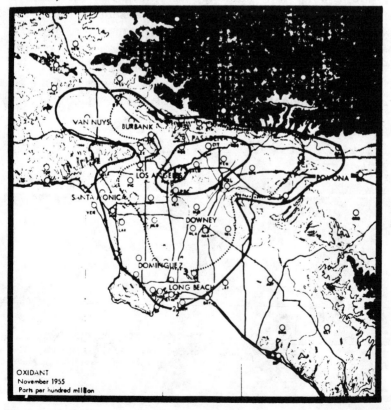

OXIDANT
November 1955
Parts per hundred million

has increased and, because of the warming of the ground, the inversion was lifting. By 4:15 P.M. the oxidant has fully developed and reached 0.30 ppm. To the connoisseur there is some satisfaction in having such a multidimensional picture of the smog, its horizontal and its vertical movement, and, in addition, its movement and changing chemical character with time.

The formation of the oxidant interested me from the beginning. The rapidly rising oxidizing property of the air during the day, the rapid decline after dark, always together with the presence of organic acids, aldehydes, organic peroxides, was intriguing. The source of these organics seemed rather obvious, but for a long time we avoided the word "gasoline" and called it hydrocarbons. Its oxidation would explain the presence of the organic oxidative products, but still we could not explain the presence of ozone. To fill the basin with ozone at concentrations of 0.4 ppm, one needs about 500 tons of ozone. Considering its half-life in the polluted area of about

Figure 8

Areal Distribution of Oxidant, Los Angeles Basin, November 1960

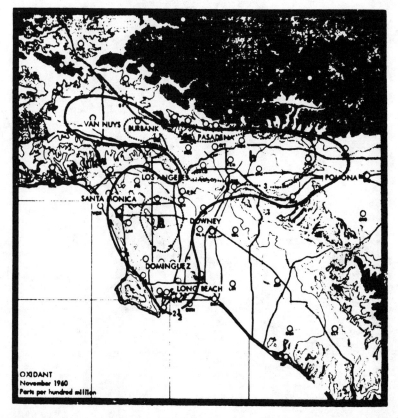

Figure 9

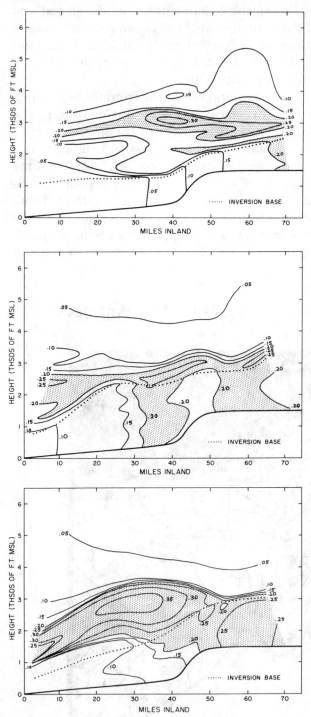

1 hour, we would need a production of several thousand tons per day. Certainly no industry or high-tension wires could produce this phenomenal quantity. The only possibility was that the ozone was formed from the major pollutants—oxides of nitrogen and hydrocarbons.

It was known that nitrogen dioxide dissociates into nitrogen oxide and atomic oxygen in sunlight, but this reaction could not account for the high concentrations actually observed. Some reaction scheme had to be found so that the nitrogen oxides would not react with the newly formed ozone. I postulated one that involved alkyl radicals produced by the atomic oxygen from the photodissociation of nitrogen dioxide.

One can visualize hydrocarbons (written as RH) attacked by the very reactive atomic oxygen to form an alkyl radical R. Present in very minute concentrations this alkyl radical can be expected to react with the surrounding oxygen molecules to form peroxyl radicals ROO. If these then react with another molecule of oxygen, *ozone* is formed.

$$NO_2 \xrightarrow{h\nu} NO + O\cdot$$

$$RH + O \longrightarrow R\cdot + \cdot OH$$

$$R\cdot + O_2 \longrightarrow ROO\cdot$$

$$ROO\cdot + O_2 \longrightarrow RO\cdot + O_3$$

I realized that such a theory would draw some fire. Knowing that my colleagues in photochemistry were still quarreling about how H and Cl combine to form hydrochloric acid, it was not likely that I was going to win a case when a few thousand different compounds—hydrocarbons and their derivatives—were involved. The easiest way out was to blow off some nitrogen dioxide and gasoline in a fumigation room in the sunlight and see what happened. As smog indicators, I used plants that were known to show distinct leaf-damage patterns when exposed to smog. Spinach, for example, would show a silvering of the underside of the leaf after a smog attack.

I hit the jackpot with the first experiment. The plants had their typical, specific markings for smog. And as a bonus I enjoyed the sweet smell of smog while tears were running down my nose. A haze developed and ozone formation was evident from the typical cracking of rubber strips. The fumigation room for quite some time became a Mecca for politicians, industrialists, and friends. Fumigating them with a good dose of artificial smog was much more effective than any theoretical explanation I could have made.

What we are dealing with here is actually a quite general type of reaction whereby the energy of the sun is trapped by one compound, called a sensitizer, and then transferred to another compound. In this way the sun is the motor that generates high-energy molecules, such as ozone and the peracyl nitrates. It is similarly responsible for the breakdown of the organic molecules into aldehydes, acids, and polymeric compounds which cause a decrease in visibility. As a chemist, I thought it would be interesting to do some chemical engineering by building the sensitizer—the light absorber —into the molecule to be decomposed. An ideal compound was one that I was quite familiar with: the essence of butter flavor.

Diacetyl is a yellow compound and has two adjacent keto groups that give strong absorption in the blue. Light dissociates it into free radicals and, in the presence of oxygen, ozone is formed. I used to demonstrate this reaction by its effect on a bent piece of rubber. At the beginning of the lecture I would put a drop of diacetyl in a round-bottomed flask in which I had suspended a piece of rubber. After 1 hour's exposure to the light, the rubber would be heavily cracked from the effect of the ozone that was formed. As in the smog reaction, we can assume that peroxyl radicals are formed which then react with oxygen to form ozone:

$$H_3C-\overset{\overset{O}{\|}}{C} \vdots \overset{\overset{O}{\|}}{C}-CH_3 \xrightarrow{\text{light}} H_3C-\overset{\underset{\underset{O}{\|}}{}}{C}\cdot-O_2$$

$$H_3C-\overset{}{\underset{\underset{O}{\|}}{C}OO\cdot} \xrightarrow{O_2} H_3C-\overset{}{\underset{\underset{O}{\|}}{C}O\cdot} + O_3$$

This same compound has served well in synthesizing PAN, the eye-irritating and plant-damaging peracetyl nitrate. Dr. Stephens from Riverside prepared this by reacting the diacetyl with nitrogen dioxide:

$$R-\overset{\overset{O}{\|}}{C}\cdot + O_2 \longrightarrow R-\overset{\overset{O}{\|}}{C}OO\cdot$$

$$R-\overset{\overset{O}{\|}}{C}-OO\cdot + NO_2 \longrightarrow R-\overset{\overset{O}{\|}}{C}-OONO_2$$

With benzoyl groups, the strongly irritating perbenzoyl nitrate PBN is formed.

One would expect similar reactions to occur with, for example, pyruvic acid, which has also two adjacent $C=O$ groups and should readily decompose with sunlight. It behaved as expected, leading us to try trimesitylene, a compound that can decompose to 3 moles of pyruvic acid when NO_2 is used as a light sensitizer. The compound did not disappoint me, and ozone was formed quite readily. It was the first of the aromatic gasoline components shown to be an ozone former.

Mesitylene

The smog reactions are often accompanied by aerosol formations, explaining part of the haze associated with smog attacks. Since free radicals are formed, a free-radical-initiated polymerization reaction could play the following role:

$$R\cdot \ + \ C{=}C \longrightarrow R{-}C{-}C\cdot$$

$$R{-}C{-}C\cdot \ + \ C{=}C \longrightarrow R{-}C{-}C{-}C{-}C\cdot \quad \text{etc.}$$

the formation of aerosol particles depends on the degree of volatility of the degradation and polymerization products. Therefore, we could expect that cyclic olefins yielding nearly non-volatile oxidation and polymerization products would be well suited for some haze experiments. And true enough, *cyclohexene* was an excellent haze producer when photooxidized in the presence of oxides of nitrogen. My prize haze producer, however, was a compound with two double bonds, a tricyclic ring system: a dimerization product of cyclopentadiene, or *dicyclopentadiene.*

Cyclopentadiene (2 molecules)   Dicyclopentadiene

And so we now believe that the sequence of the reactions leading to smog be pictured as in Figure 10. The primary reaction is a dissociation of NO_2 with the formation of atomic oxygen. This active oxygen, assisted by excited oxygen, peroxyl radical, oxidizes the

Figure 10

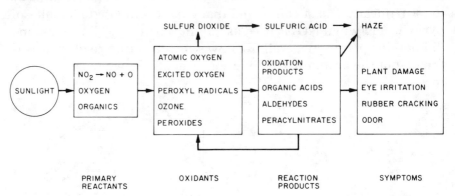

organic materials and also sulfur dioxide. These reactions and those among the various reaction products give rise to the symptoms usually associated with smog. This scheme is supported by experiments, such as long-path infrared measurements on the decomposition of 3-methylheptane (Figure 11). You see how readily the compound is degraded. The methyl group appears as formic acid

Figure 11

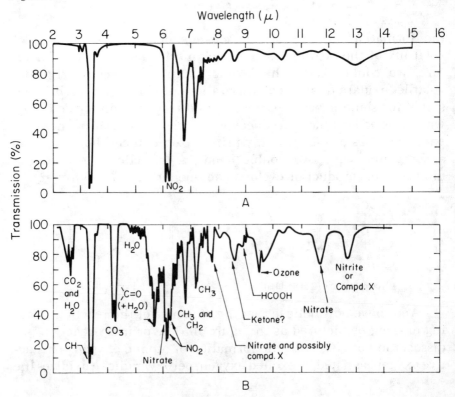

Table 3

Inorganic		Organic Chain Reactions	
(1) $NO_2 + hv$	$= NO + O$	(10) $R\cdot + O_2$	$= RO_2\cdot$
(2) $O + O_2$	$= O_3$	(11) $RO_2\cdot + O_2$	$= RO\cdot + O_3$
(3) $2NO + O_2$	$= 2NO_2$	(12) $RO\cdot + RH$	$= ROH + R\cdot$
(4) $O_3 + NO$	$= O_2 + NO_2$	(13) $RO_2\cdot + RH$	$= ROOH + R\cdot$
(5) $O_3 + 2NO_2$	$= N_2O_5 + O_2$	(14) $2RO_2\cdot$	$= 2RO\cdot + O_2$
(6) $O + H_2O(g)$	$= 2HO\cdot$		
Generation of Organic Free Radicals		**Consumption of Organic Free Radicals**	
(7) $O_3 + olefins$	$= products$	(15) $2RO\cdot$	$= aldehyde + alcohol$
(8) $O + RH$	$= R\cdot + OH\cdot$	(16) $RO\cdot + NO$	$= RONO$
(9) $OH\cdot + RH$	$= R\cdot + H_2O$	(17) $RO_2\cdot + NO$	$= RO_2 NO$
			$= RO\cdot + NO_2$

and CO_2, the rest of the molecule as a ketone. We see further the appearance of PAN and ozone.

The scheme in Table 3 gives a simplified version of the primary reactions followed by chain and termination reactions. Other schemes have been presented and only one of these, which was postulated by Dr. Wayne, is presented here. They all contain the essential *peroxyl-radical formation.* The kinetic model consists of 13 generalized chemical reactions and is a variation of the mechanism proposed by Wayne:

$$NO_2 + hv = NO + O\cdot \qquad (1)$$
$$O\cdot + O_2 + M = O_3 + M \qquad (2)$$
$$NO + O_3 = NO_2 + O_2 \qquad (3)$$
$$HC + O\cdot = HCO^* \qquad (4)$$
$$HCO^* + O_2 = XR \qquad (5)$$
$$XR + hv = R\cdot + HCO\cdot + X\cdot \qquad (6)$$
$$XO_2\cdot + NO = XO\cdot + NO_2 \qquad (7)$$
$$XO\cdot + NO = X\cdot + NO_2 \qquad (8)$$
$$XO\cdot + HC = HCO^* + X\cdot \qquad (9)$$
$$XO\cdot + NO_2 = XONO_2 \qquad (10)$$
$$X\cdot + O_2 = XO_2\cdot \qquad (11)$$
$$XO\cdot + O_2 = X\cdot + C_3 \qquad (12)$$
$$O_3 + HC = (products) + XR \qquad (13)$$

We can sèe here how nature is rebalancing the composition of the atmosphere. The original pollutants, hydrocarbons, and their oxidation products are oxidized. The carbon chains are chewed down carbon by carbon until nothing but carbon dioxide remains:

$$
\begin{array}{l}
\xrightarrow[O_2]{\text{SUN}} \quad C-C-C-C-C-C- \\
\qquad\qquad\qquad\quad\downarrow \\
\xrightarrow[O_2]{\text{SUN}} \quad C-C-C-C-C- \qquad +O_3 +CO_2 \\
\qquad\qquad\qquad\quad\downarrow \\
\xrightarrow[O_2]{\text{SUN}} \quad C-C-C-C- \qquad +O_3 +CO_2 \\
\qquad\qquad\qquad\quad\downarrow \\
\xrightarrow[O_2]{\text{SUN}} \quad C-C-C- \qquad +O_3 +CO_2 \\
\qquad\qquad\qquad\quad\downarrow \\
\xrightarrow[O_2]{\text{SUN}} \quad C-C- \qquad +O_3 +CO_2 \\
\qquad\qquad\qquad\quad\downarrow \\
\qquad\qquad\quad C- \qquad +O_3 +CO_2
\end{array}
$$

For practical reasons, it was important to know the rates of reactions at various concentrations of the reactants. As a model, the reaction of NO_2 and 3-methylheptane was chosen (Figure 12). When irradiated ozone is formed and the rate of its formation at different concentrations is measured, this rate varies greatly. Ozone formation as measured by the rubber-cracking method at about 0.1 ppm NO_2 came to a maximum at about 3 ppm and approached zero again at 10 ppm.

This behavior caused a great deal of controversy. My colleagues who tried to reproduce this reaction were not aware that the ozone formation is limited to an area of very low NO_2 concentration. It is at these low concentrations that the reactive intermediates have an appreciable transitory existence. Notions about the reactivity of compounds are often colored by the laboratory experience. Most chemists are used to working at relatively high concentrations, often in the order of 10 or more percent. This is 1 million times more concentrated than we are dealing with in the polluted atmosphere, where we are talking about a fraction of parts per million (Figure 13). Under these conditions, compounds such as olefins, ozone, oxides of nitrogen, and sulfur dioxide can exist together for quite some time. The coexistence of quite reactive substances is explained on the basis of the fundamental laws of chemical kinetics, whereby the reaction rate is proportional to the concentration of the reactants.

Figure 12

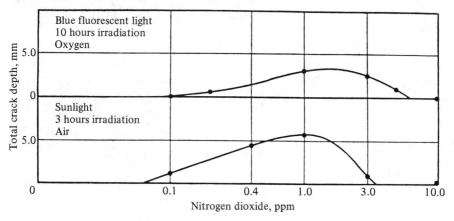

Figure 13

Average concentrations during days of eye irritation in downtown Los Angeles. Hydrocarbons, aldehydes, and ozone for 1953–1954. Nitric oxide and nitrogen dioxide for 1958. From data of the Los Angeles County Air Pollution Control District.

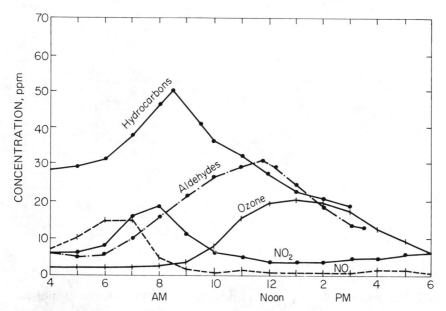

A fast reaction in smog formation is the one between nitrogen oxide (NO) and ozone. As the ozone forms, the NO disappears and the NO_2 takes its place. The study of the rates of reaction at various concentrations of oxides of nitrogen developed into a long, drawn-out controversy, especially with chemists of General Motors, who thought that it would be better to increase the NO_x and glide down

Figure 14

Typical concentration of unburned hydrocarbons, carbon monoxide, and nitrogen oxides as function of air: fuel ratio. Car speed 60 mph.

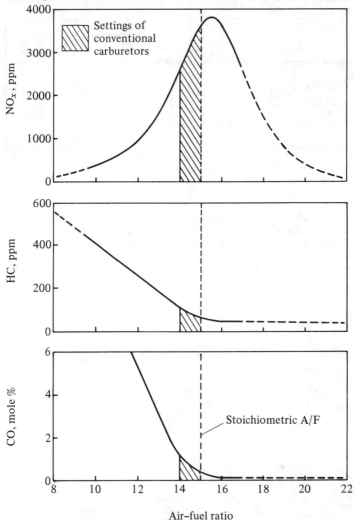

the hill to higher atmospheric concentrations. This desire coincided with an auto-exhaust control program of leaning the air–fuel mixture which caused a drastic increase in the emission of nitrogen oxides (Figure 14).

My work in the fumigation room had clearly indicated that the area of relatively high concentration of the nitrogen oxides was unbearable. My simple fumigation room with its manual adjustment of flowmeters made me a part of the experiment while GM's

Figure 15

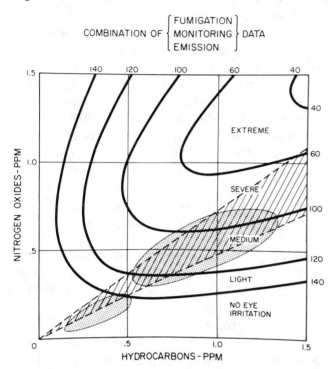

COMBINATION OF {FUMIGATION / MONITORING / EMISSION} DATA

elaborate equipment did not allow the experimenter to enjoy their suggestion. Simplicity in experimentation does sometimes pay off!

A good way of presenting rate-of-formation data is by making horizontal cuts through the three-dimensional plot, drawing what I have called iso-irritation lines, Figure 15. You will notice that the curves are somewhat distorted hyperbolas, but near the origin they fulfill the requirement that the effect is proportional to the product of the concentrations of the hydrocarbons and the oxides of nitrogen. It is clear that decrease of the hydrocarbons with a simultaneous rise of the oxides of nitrogen is no cure. This is exactly what the auto industry has been doing the past few years.

It is of interest, of course, to know where we are on these graphs when there is smog and when the sky is clear. For this we have to consult the monitoring data from the County Air Pollution District. The large ellipse in Figure 15 contains hydrocarbon and NO_x values measured when the oxidant value is greater than 0.4 ppm. This means heavy smog with irritation. The small ellipse shows clear days with oxidant data lower than 0.1 ppm. These ellipses are lined up in a straight line, as indicated in Figure 15, because the ambient air concentration is proportional to the inversion height. When the height is 4000 feet, the concentration of both components is one fourth of that of a 1000-foot inversion. It is now clear that the only thing to do to clear up the smog is to move the big ellipse down to the position of the small ellipse. This means a reduction of about 75 percent of each of the contaminants. Considering that it takes some ten years to accomplish this, we need a 90 percent correction, which is exactly what the Nixon–Muskie bill prescribes for 1975.

It would be wonderful it we could apply the present control technology to the older cars on the road. It takes about 10 to 12 years to renew these cars, and an inexpensive device to accomplish this would be most welcome. Although various manufacturers have attempted to develop such a device which would cost less than a legal $65.00, up until now there is none available. Several of these devices showed unpleasant effects on the drivability which could lead to serious accidents. At present, only one of these proposed devices is still being considered. There should be some incentive, considering that there are some 8 million cars to be equipped and that at $65.00 each this means a half-a-billion-dollar business.

On the whole, the control attempts of the auto industry have been accelerated greatly. It seems to me in talking to automobile engineers that they have found a new toy to play with. After all, a good engineer gets tired of designing fancy doorknobs, hiding bumpers, and doing all kinds of things to doll up the exterior of the car. Now they have found a new problem, a most difficult one: how to reduce the nitrogen oxide, carbon monoxide, and hydrocarbon emission at the same time. This problem has now been partially licked by exhaust burners, better fuel distribution, and leaner air–fuel mixtures to reduce the organics and retard spark timing and exhaust recirculation to reduce the oxides of nitrogen. Great progress has been made toward reaching the short-range goals, but many experts believe that a catalytic approach is the final answer, and this is the basis for the demand of the removal of lead from gasoline.

While there is distinct progress in the engineering control of auto emissions, similar progress is being made in the control of emissions from stationary sources. To give only one example, the concentration of the oxides of nitrogen from power-plant combustion has been reduced by a factor of 5 to 10 in recent years by applying some of the same techniques as are used in the automobile: in this case, so-called secondary combustion, which consists of burning 90 percent of the fuel with a limited amount of air, followed by introducing excess air. This results in a 50 percent reduction of the concentration of the oxides of nitrogen. Recirculation of some exhaust air further reduces the peak flame temperature, with reduction of the NO content of the stack gases. The local districts have launched a new effort in the control of dust and oxides of sulfur emission, and all these efforts must pay off in an improvement of the quality of the air.

But this is not the end of the story. The population increases about 2 percent per year; this is doubled in 25 years. The demand for power is increasing even faster; it is doubling every 8 years. At present, we don't know how we can reduce power-plant emission further except to go to nuclear plants. What will happen if we have twice as many power plants in 8 years and in another 8 years, four times as many? This is the crux of the problem: growth of population and a demand for more services of all kinds. There is very little evidence of planning for the future; *growth* is still considered the prime goal of our existence. The planning for balanced transportation systems, sensible land use, setting aside large park areas, fresh-air reserves, are still subordinate to the desire of short-term profits regardless of the consequences. These are the tasks that your generation has to face. (Perhaps the international weather symbol recently proposed for smog

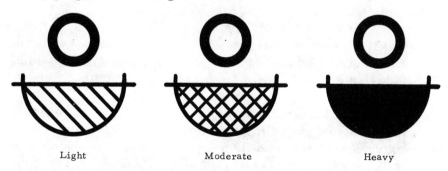

| Light | Moderate | Heavy |

will become obsolete in your lifetime.) It is a big battle, but breathing clear air is worth the effort! I believe it can be done!

/Discussion/

SHELDON FRIEDLANDER: Can I supplement what you said by a few remarks about the particulate matter which might be of interest? We've made some measurements over the last couple of years on the particulate components of the atmosphere which might be of interest to you, to give you a feeling of where the visibility reduction has its origin. What we find is that of about 100 micrograms per cubic meter of particles in the atmosphere, only about 5 percent of that, 5 micrograms, comes from natural background, sea salt coming in from the ocean, and about 10–15 percent comes from wind-raised dust. The rest of it, about 80 percent, comes from man-made sources; for example, about 17 percent is from the automobile, about 10 percent from aircraft, about 15 percent from power plants, and about 10 percent from industrial sources. And finally about 30 percent is actually formed in the atmosphere—nitrates, sulfates, organic materials, formed in the atmosphere by chemical reactions. So you get a general picture of the causes of the visibility problem.

QUESTION FROM AUDIENCE: Do you have any research evidence on eventual dispersal of pollutants and what happens when they are swept off into the desert and over the ocean?

HAAGEN-SMIT: Some work has been done (not enough) and it is generally agreed that compounds such as the oxides of sulfur and nitrogen have a relatively short life, estimated to be a few days. These pollutants are converted into sulfates and nitrates. Some of the haze droplets found in Riverside contain quite some nitrates. It is easy to detect calcium and ammonium sulfates on our windows. The rest of these more stable reaction products will settle out and be removed by precipitation.

QUESTION: What about organic acids?

HAAGEN-SMIT: I did some work on various organic acids. Acetic acid in the presence of oxides of nitrogen does form ozone, from which I conclude that it is unstable and is broken down eventually to CO_2 and water.

The combination of nitrogen dioxide and sunlight is a powerful oxidizing agent and even straight-chain paraffins are degraded. In this photochemical decomposition, normal octane, for example, is apparently hydroxylated at one of the end carbon atoms. The octyl nitrate formed is further decomposed. I expect a carbon-by-carbon breakdown to continue until we have nothing else but CO_2 and water. There is no indication of a carbon monoxide buildup, and its lifetime has been estimated at a few days.

QUESTION: As someone involved in the administrative end, too, what do you think are the possibilities for other kinds of control besides direct regulation?

HAAGEN-SMIT: I am glad you bring up this question. What I am doing is like giving an aspirin for a chronic ailment. The cause of our trouble lies much deeper. It is the problem of our ever-expanding and more crowded metropolitan areas, no planning, or inadequate planning, guided by personal profit and the slogan that "growth is good."

The lack of coordinated means of transportation, the lack of adequate breathing centers in the form of parks, antiquated local governments, and tax laws promoting the destruction of the countryside and valuable farmland are causes. It is evident everywhere. It is your generation that has to fight for a better system of managing our urban centers. Such change does not come easy, but the battle must be fought and air-pollution control is only one of the many battlefronts. It is encouraging that in both federal and state governments, steps are underway now to bridge the gap between classical departments, such as Health, Urban Affairs, and Transportation. How successful this marriage will be remains to be seen, but we can hope. There is always the ballot box.

QUESTION: What do you think about a pollution tax that might provide incentive to develop low-pollution technology? Would it help if we gave inventors support or a tax break for developing clean cars?

HAAGEN-SMIT: I don't really believe very much in this kind of tax-incentive system. You could interpret it as a tax to pollute. In the case of the automobile control, one could think of a tax on gasoline, but it has to be a pretty drastic tax, maybe doubling the price, before people start sharing rides or start asking for a more adequate transportation system. I wish we could follow this route, but the chances are quite slim. Proposition 18 didn't even pass and that was only a 1-cent increase in tax. The second part of your question suggests that perhaps a tax incentive or subsidy could be useful in the development of a clean car. We should realize that the emissions of automobiles are steadily going down, and by 1975 the cars will be quite clean in hydrocarbons, CO, oxides of nitrogen, and particulate matter, including lead. The work at the automobile companies has finally gone into high gear and the state and federal laws do not allow any slackening of the pace. The companies are developing alternative power plants for cars, but steam, Stirling, or Wankel engines have to compete with a well-entrenched, clean, 1975 engine. I don't see that government funds would make a significant contribution. Nevertheless, some support is being given to the development of alternatives. I do like the idea of the electric cars. The trouble is first that they cannot compete with what we expect from a modern car and second that we have to produce electricity somewhere. Already the demand is such that we will have to double the power production every 8 years. Instead of the present 10,000 megawatts, we will have to produce 20,000 before 1980. Maybe here we can apply the tax break.

QUESTION: I have a report from the Technical Committee of the Air Resources Board. This report says that the public must be apprised, warned, that they will continue to be exposed to a level of oxidants that affects their health. Now this came out in September 1970, and I don't remember any big splash from the *Los Angeles Times* saying that my health was being impaired by continually exposing myself to this level of oxidants. Is the Air Resources Board going to make a big deal out of this?

HAAGEN-SMIT: It is difficult to get these things in the newspapers. When somebody proposes aerial sewers in all the freeways, he gets a whole page in the *Times*; on the other hand, when we try to give facts, there is little interest. This is serious, as people must learn to understand the real cause of our pollution troubles. I must say, though, that the newspaper participation has been quite helpful, and they, together with various civic groups, have been actively supporting the Board in passing needed legislation. Experienced legislators, like Assemblyman Lanterman, have been working for public transit for many, many years, but he needs support. It will be a hard and long battle before we have a rapid-transit system matching our freeways, but I am convinced that we will win when we press hard enough.

QUESTION: What kind of transportation system would you recommend as being feasible for some time in the future for an area as spread out as Los Angeles?

HAAGEN-SMIT: To begin with, I don't think that it is an objection that Los Angeles is spread out. Public transit is excellent to connect high-density centers. I will settle for anything that moves about at 60 to 100 mph and takes me where I want to go. I don't think we need far-out types, just give me a fast electric train like they have in Japan (I even like the New York subways). I am very much encouraged by the progress made in San Francisco. This might be just the incentive needed here: We can't let San Francisco pass us by!

NORMAN H. BROOKS

is professor of environmental science and civil engineering. He received his undergraduate degree in mathematics and master's degree in civil engineering at Harvard University, and his Ph.D. in civil engineering and physics at Caltech in 1954. He is a consultant to many firms and government agencies on design problems of outfalls for sewage and cooling-water discharges. His own research is concerned with problems of hydraulics related to water-quality management, turbulence, and diffusion and density-stratified flows.

NORMAN H. BROOKS

Energy
and the Environment

KUPPERMANN: I want to introduce our speaker for today, Professor Norman Brooks. Dr. Brooks received a B.Sc. degree in mathematics and a master's degree in civil engineering from Harvard, and earned a Ph.D. from Caltech in civil engineering with a minor in physics. As you can see, his educational background is appallingly lacking—there is no degree in chemistry at all. It's probably one of the components of his strength. Most of Professor Brooks' professional career was spent at Caltech, where he is a Professor of Environmental Science and Civil Engineering and chairman of Environmental Engineering Science faculty. His specialty is the field of water resources development and pollution control, of which he is a leading expert, and he is presently a member of the Assembly Science and Technology Advisory Council of the California Legislature. His input into the State Legislature should help the state solve many of its problems.

BROOKS: I do have to confess that I don't know much chemistry. I don't know if I should be here at this Chemistry and Society Seminar. Not only do I not know any chemistry, but I have doubts whether I understand society.

I might start out by telling you about the Assembly Advisory Council on Science and Technology. It consists of 16 members—about 11 scientists and engineers and about 5 social scientists; cutting it another way, you can say that about 11 are from universities and about 5 from industry. This council is the only one of its kind in the country—it is advisory to a legislature, not to an executive agency of the government, and it is supported by an NSF grant. We've only been in existence about a year and are just settling in.

The legislature has sent the science council a list of areas where we might help them. It reads something like this: natural disasters, agriculture business, manpower needs, criminology, health care, welfare problems, urban development, transportation, environmental problems, education, housing—in fact, the only thing not on the list is off-track betting!

But there seems to be a conflict of philosophies. The legislature tends to be responsive to rather short-range problems and it tends to be compartmentalized in its thinking. The science council, on the other hand, takes a longer, more comprehensive view of things. Whatever question we discuss, whether it be about housing or environment or education or natural disasters, we always reach the same ultimate question: What do we want California to be like fifty years from now? The next question is: What will the population be?, followed by: Who is going to be running California? But planning at the statewide level leads to problems. Better planning here means less responsibility at the city and county level. A typical example is determining the location of a new power plant. Many communities may need the power but no one wants to live near the plant. Does each community have veto power? There will be some things like this for which it may be necessary for the State to intervene, and hard decisions will have to be made.

Currently the council is using special panels to look at four major problems: population growth, health care, solid-waste management, and energy. In addition, a subcommittee exists to help the legislature take a broader view of environmental matters.

Today I shall discuss the energy problem and give you my recommendations for an energy policy. In California, as in the whole United States, satisfying society's growing demand for energy has become a critical problem. I shall explain why I believe it is urgent for society to reduce drastically the growth rate of energy usage and to recognize that energy is a scarce resource, not so much because of limitations of fuel supplies, but because of the finiteness of the environment.

The woes of the electric utility industry make daily reading in the nation's press. The power companies have not been able to supply all the electricity the public demands during certain critical periods—for example, during heat waves, when air conditioners, refrigerators, and electric fans add heavier power loads. The result is more frequent blackouts and brownouts (voltage reductions) as the power companies struggle to keep the load within the limits of generating capacity.

The utilities have faced an array of difficult and coincidental problems trying to keep up with the ever-increasing demand. There have been long delays in delivery and installation of nuclear-generating units, following the unusually large orders for nuclear equipment in 1966 and 1967 which swamped that new section of the power-generating equipment industry. In some new large conventional units, operational failures have occurred unexpectedly. Power companies have found that shutdowns for maintenance have been more difficult to schedule because high peaks of demand now occur both in winter and summer.

Fuel delivery has suddenly become a problem for the utilities. For air-pollution control, they must use low-sulfur coal, but the supply is inadequate. New mine-safety regulations have curtailed some mining operations, and caused defaults in some coal supply contracts. Even railroad coal cars are becoming scarce, and some utilities are having to purchase their own cars to be assured of deliveries. Because of attractive prices, more coal is being exported to Japan. Whereas utilities used to have several months' coal supply on hand, they now have just a few weeks' supply and sometimes only a few days' advance supply. Fuel oil has also been in short supply because of oil import restrictions and the tanker shortage caused by closure of the Suez Canal and the interruption of the Trans-Arabian Pipeline.

Concern about the environment has caused a tightening of air- and water-quality standards for power-plant discharges. Currently there are arguments about the adequacy of radiation standards for nuclear plants. For those who must plan capital expenditures and their repayment for decades into the future, the fluidity of environmental requirements presents a difficult planning problem.

Power-plant siting is an even more urgent problem of the industry. Conservationists and the power industry have had many lively confrontations over siting of plants and transmission lines in the last few years. In general, these controversies have not contributed to recent power shortages because the lead time between final site selection and on-line operation is often five years or more; but a few years hence we shall be able to say that power shortages were caused by arguments over power-plant sites.

Electric power is, of course, just one part of society's total energy usage. Not only is fuel burned to generate electricity at central power stations, but it is also used directly for heating buildings, for transportation, and in industry.

Figure 1

Historic Growth of U.S. Annual Energy Consumption with a High and a Low Projection to the Year 2000.

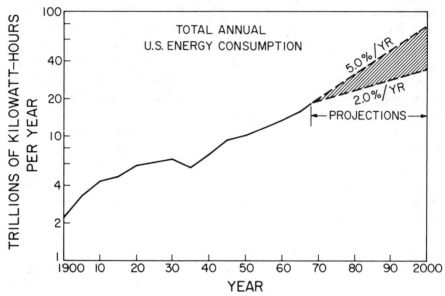

The total energy consumption in the United States in 1968 was 17.8 trillion kilowatt-hours (kWh)—equivalent to a continuous average use of 10,000 watts (W) per person. In 1900 it was 2.2 trillion kWh —an overall average growth in the intervening years of 3.1 percent per year (compounded). But in the period 1935 to 1968, the rate was 3.6 percent per year, and in the most recent four years, 1964–1968, the rate of growth was 4.9 percent per year. A growth rate of 5 percent per year in the future would lead to an energy consumption of 76 trillion kWh in the year 2000—over four times the present yearly usage. If the growth rate were only 2 percent per year, the figure for A.D. 2000 would be less than half as much—34 trillion kWh. The important point is that the growth rate, when compounded over many years, has an enormous leverage on how our resources and environment are going to be affected.

I am not a "futurist" because I do not think that we must plan for whatever the demands may be; on the contrary, it will be necessary for society to *control* this growth rate to keep energy use and its environmental effects within tolerable limits.

The primary sources of the energy were, for 1968:

Crude petroleum	40.7%
Natural gas	32.1
Coal	21.9
Natural gas liquids	3.8
Hydroelectric generation	1.3
Nuclear energy	0.2
Total (17.8 x 10^{12} kWh)	100.0%

Fossil fuels accounted for 98.5 percent of the total, while nuclear energy was only 0.2 percent. The nuclear fraction will grow very rapidly in the near future as it displaces fossil fuels in production of electricity. Hydroelectric power is also a very small percentage and will probably continue to stay small because most of the feasible hydro sites have already been built. It should be noted that hydropower is the only energy source which uses the current energy budget of the earth rather than energy stored from some other geologic age. There are other small sources of energy—wood, refuse, geothermal heat—which do not usually appear in the statistical summaries, but the amount for the United States is probably only a few tenths of 1 percent of the total. Direct beneficial use of solar energy (agriculture, drying, heating, etc.) cannot be computed; the amounts mentioned here refer only to man-made energy-distribution systems.

Of the total energy consumed in 1968, only 8.0 percent—1.43 trillion kWh—was converted to electric power. However, an additional 14 percent of the total was discharged as waste heat by the thermal power stations, operating at an average efficiency of 33 percent. Hence 22 percent of the total energy supply was used to run the electric power systems.

Electric power production by utilities was 1.33 trillion kWh—a growth of 9 percent over the preceding year. (The small remainder —0.10 trillion kWh—was produced by industry for in-plant use.) For the period 1920–1968, the average growth rate was 7.5 percent per year—or doubling every 9.5 years. If the demand continues to grow at 7 percent per year, the production by utilities will have to increase over fourfold by 1990 to 5.9 trillion kWh. Even a much lower projection of only 3.8 percent growth per year leads to 3.0 trillion kWh. The difference between these two projections for 1990 is more than twice the current production, which illustrates the enormous impact that the growth rate has on problems of power-plant siting. How many sites will *really* be needed in the future?

Figure 2

Growth of Electrical Energy Production by Utilities from 1920 to 1968, with Range of Projections to 1990.

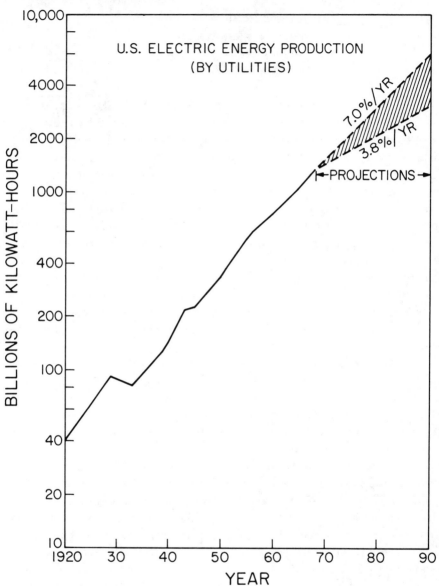

The electrical energy produced by utilities in 1968 came from the following primary sources:

Coal	51.7%
Gas	22.9
Oil	7.8
Nuclear	0.9
Hydro	16.7
Total (1.33 x 10¹² kWh)	100.0%

By contrast, hydropower accounted for 36 percent in 1945. In the future, as in the past few years, the vast majority of the new installa-

Figure 3

Historic Growth of Installed Capacity and Peak Load, with Projection by the Federal Power Commission.

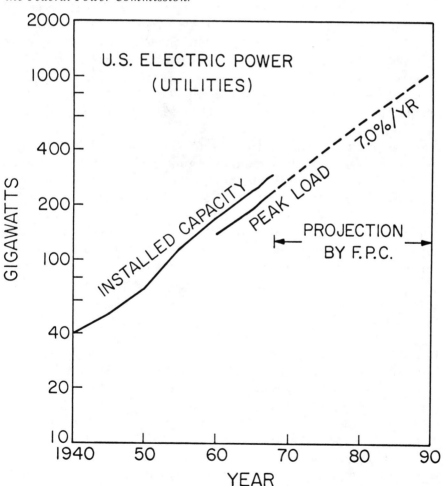

tions will be thermal power, with nuclear power becoming a rapidly increasing part. Although practically all the feasible conventional hydropower sites have been developed, large pumped-storage plants for peaking are being built and will be sought increasingly in the future to allow higher load factors at thermal plants by pumping water up for storage during off-peak hours.

Gross electrical generating capacity (not allowing for shutdowns for maintenance and repairs) is just a very few years ahead of the peak load. At the present growth rate the peak-load forecast for 1990 is over 1000 gigawatts (gW) [or 1,000,000 megawatts (MW)], compared to the 1968 peak of 243 gW.

At thermal power plants the maximum size of a *single* generating unit has increased from 200 MW in 1950 to 1300 MW at present (or the equivalent of the entire generating capacity at Hoover Dam). The largest power plants may have several of these huge units; for example, Brown's Ferry, TVA, 3400 MW (under construction); and Point Conception, S. California Edison Co., 6600 MW (being planned). Still larger units are not anticipated because there are few additional economies of scale to be realized and because an extremely large generating unit can be a disadvantage because its breakdown takes out too large a fraction of a given system capacity.

The power problems of the State of California have recently been summarized by the Resources Agency, which projects growth at 8 percent per year until 1990, at which time the demand will have increased fivefold over 1969. Per capita demand is predicted to rise from 1.17 to 4.0 kW (about 6 percent per year compounded), while population growth is projected at 2 percent per year. Considering the current difficulties of finding acceptable sites, it seems almost impossible to believe that siting for over 90,000 MW additional can be accomplished in 21 years. Furthermore, it is hard to believe that we really need three to four times as much power per person—and can afford it.

I suspect that predictions of future power demands have often been self-fulfilling prophecies. If a power company decides to build large new generating stations to meet "projected" needs, it urgently requires that the new demand be realized on schedule in order to make a return on the company's capital investments, and it will conduct the necessary advertising and promotional campaigns to achieve the expected growth in business.

If the growth rate could be cut in half—to 4 percent per year— the positive impact would be enormous. The projected peak demand in 1990 would be only 52,000 MW—63,000 MW less than the State's

Table 1

Electric Power in California

HISTORIC ELECTRIC POWER DEMAND
FOR STATE OF CALIFORNIA

Year	Peak power demand[a] (megawatts)	Population[b] (thousands)	Ratio: kW per capita
1940	2,300	6,907	0.33
1950	5,300	10,586	0.50
1960	11,500	15,717	0.73
1965	17,400	18,207	0.96
1969	22,800	19,476	1.17

HISTORIC GROWTH RATES (State of California)

Years	Peak power demand	Population	Ratio: kW per capita
1940–50	8.7%/yr	4.3%/yr	4.4%/yr
1950–60	8.0	4.1	3.9
1960–65	8.6	3.0	5.6
1965–69	7.0	1.7	5.3

[a] Data from State of California, Resources Agency, "Siting Thermal Power Plants in California," Feb. 15, 1970.

[b] Data from "California Population, 1969," State of California, Dept. of Finance, December 1969.

projection. This would still allow a 2 percent per year increase in demand per person. If this reduction in growth rate could be accomplished, the reduction in capital costs for power plants and transmission lines would be about $20 billion dollars in 21 years—and not only do the capital costs keep going up, but so also does the intangible damage to the environment.

Even if we could survive the expansion to the year 1990, how many more doublings every 8 to 10 years can we stand? We do not need more research to prove that the environment remains finite. Its capacity to absorb wastes never doubles—it just remains fixed. Can we realistically expect technology to solve the environmental problems and side effects of energy usage?116

Why does electric power get so much emphasis when it accounts for only 22 percent of all the energy consumption? It is because the power plants are such concentrated energy centers that the power-plant surroundings are subject to more intense environmental effects than other places where energy conversion and usage is more diffuse—as in our homes, businesses, and automobiles. There is a tendency to replace small-scale combustion of fuels—in furnaces, stoves, automobiles—with electricity. In other words, instead of distributing so much fuel to individual users, we burn the fuel at a central power station and distribute electricity instead. This is an environmental tradeoff, for while you relieve the problems at one place where electricity is substituted for fuel, you add to the problems of siting enough power plants and controlling their emissions. Electricity is also a great help in solving other environmental problems—such as building and running sewage-treatment plants. Thus in the *long* run the strategy for locating, building, and operating central power stations assumes critical importance.

Many adverse environmental effects are associated with electric power generation. One set of problems is associated with the mining, processing, and transporting of fuels to the power plants; another set arises from the combustion of fossil fuels and disposal of ashes and residuals extracted from the flue gases (for air-pollution control); more problems arise from the transportation, processing, and disposal of spent nuclear fuel elements; another major problem is the dispersal of waste heat; and finally there are a multitude of land use and aesthetic questions associated with power plants and transmission lines. The problem of waste heat should be considered in detail because of its fundamental nature.

At every thermal power plant a very substantial amount of waste heat is rejected—by means of cooling-water systems—into the surrounding environment. Both fossil fuel and nuclear plants operate on a steam cycle which converts part of the heat from a hot source (the furnace or the reactor) into work (electric power), and the remaining heat is discharged into a cool sink (the power-plant environs). Typical thermal efficiencies of new plants are as shown in Table 2.

By the laws of thermodynamics, higher efficiencies in a steam cycle can only be achieved by operating at higher steam temperatures and pressures. Efficiencies of nuclear-powered steam plants

Table 2
Thermal Efficiencies of New Plants

	Thermal Efficiency	Waste heat per unit electrical output
Conventional (fossil fuel)	35–40%	1.5–1.8
Nuclear	30–35%	1.8–2.3

will probably catch up to conventional steam plants in another decade, as operating experience will permit using higher temperatures in the steam cycle. But limitations on materials and safety will prevent any dramatic improvements above 40 percent for the presently used steam cycle. Any possible replacement of the steam cycle by more direct means of electrochemical conversion for *large* central generating stations is at least two decades away, as the technology does not exist today. Also, direct conversion of nuclear energy to electricity without use of the steam cycle is not likely very soon; the future use of fusion energy will still probably be coupled with a steam cycle.

Thus, the waste-heat problem will be with us for a substantial period of time, and technological change in power generation cannot be expected to solve the problem for us. But there is another more fundamental waste-heat problem arising from consumption of electricity. Practically all uses of electricity ultimately lead to conversion of the energy back to heat; it occurs directly for electric space heating, electric stoves, electric furnaces, and the like, and indirectly for lighting, transportation, power tools, and so on. (To be sure, a small amount of energy is locked up in increased potential energy—mechanical or chemical—and some electromagnetic radiation—light and radio—escapes to space, but these are estimated to be only a very few percent of society's total consumption of electrical energy.) Thus, we may think of a power plant of 40 percent efficiency as releasing 60 percent of the heat in a concentrated dose at the power plant site and the other 40 percent over the points of use, primarily the urban areas.

If by some miracle all power plants could be made 100 percent efficient, the total heat release would be cut back to about 35 percent of what it is now. But if the power demand keeps doubling every 10 years, the gain in efficiency would be all used up in just 15 years of continued growth. This illustrates that any technological breakthrough in environmental control is equivalent to a one-time gain of time which can be wiped out by unchecked growth in production.

The waste heat from electricity is but part of the total waste heat released by all forms of energy use by society. The density of heat released in urban areas has already increased atmospheric temperatures significantly. Ultimately the excess heat is diffused in the atmosphere and radiated to space. On a *local* basis the total waste heat released is substantial (for example, about 5 percent of solar radiation in the City of Los Angeles), but on a *global* basis it is still very small (less than 0.01 percent of insolation at the surface).

In fact, heat as a pollutant has a unique characteristic. Because of the basic laws of thermodynamics there is no treatment as such; any efforts to concentrate it (by heat pumps) simply require more mechanical energy, which means more waste heat is generated at the power plants. Other types of environmental pollution can be alleviated by various processes, which usually consume power and ultimately produce waste heat. *Thus, heat is an ultimate residual of society's activities.*

The waste heat rejected from power plants is unusually concentrated compared to the overall release of heat by society. For example, at the proposed 6600-MW nuclear power station at Point Conception on the California coast, the waste heat will be 13,000 MW (thermal), equivalent to insolation on about 70 square kilometers of the ocean (assuming 100 percent load factor at the power plant, and insolation at 400 langleys/day $= 193$ MW/km^2).

Thermal power plants use cooling water to transfer heat from the condensers (on the low-pressure side of the turbines) to the environment. Once-through systems, which are the least expensive, take water from the environment and return it about 10° to 15°C hotter. Freshwater sources have been frequently used in the past, but with stringent thermal requirements (such as not more than a 3°C rise), there are few remaining opportunities to use once-through freshwater cooling for new major plants of several thousand megawatts. Most rivers simply do not have enough flow to provide sufficient dilution during critical summer months, and those that do (like the Tennessee) are already being used extensively for cooling.

Lakes and reservoirs can be good heat sinks, but the currents are often too small to provide good advection of heat away from the plant sites. Furthermore, lake biota and water quality are particularly sensitive to thermal changes. For Lake Michigan, for example, the new rules now being proposed are so strict that new large power plants will be forced to use cooling ponds or cooling towers.

Many estuaries are also too small to take large additional heat loads, and increased temperatures aggravate water-quality problems. The open ocean is still an excellent heat sink, but increased attention is needed for development of logical temperature criteria and effective diffusion structures for hot-water discharge.

In once-through cooling systems the natural water environment is being used as a giant heat exchanger between the power plant and the atmosphere. Thus, in setting thermal requirements and designing cooling-water outfalls, more attention should be given to the next step in the heat-transfer chain. Some questions:

1. Is it desirable to minimize the temperature rise in the receiving water by wide dispersal of the heat?

2. Should the transfer of heat to the atmosphere be maximized (by keeping the temperature increment high instead of low)?

3. Should discharge be arranged to avoid complete "blockage" of a waterway with heated water?

4. Should waste heat be stored below thermoclines in lakes and oceans to avoid any direct effect on surface temperatures during the summer?

The current regulatory practice by FWQA (the Federal Water Quality Administration) and the states is the specification of maximum temperature increments in the receiving water (objective 1), but this may be contrary to desirable objectives 2 and 3. Furthermore, following objective 4 in lakes might have serious consequences for the annual regime of a lake, although temperature increment requirements are satisfied. Within the overall limits of the heat-assimilation capacity, there are various strategies for design of outfalls to control the heat distribution in the environment —such as submerged outfall diffusers for high dilution or channel outlets for surface spreading of hot water with little dilution.

It is urgent that we have a better understanding of the ecological effects of heat in each case, and find out whether it is better to disperse waste heat widely (disturb a vast region just a little) or to set aside a much smaller aquatic region to be heated significantly, allowing other regions to remain undisturbed. Millions of dollars are going to be spent for thermal pollution control for ecological objectives that are not yet defined or understood. Even when we do understand the ecology, there remains the problem of evaluating tradeoffs—how much disturbance of aquatic life should be tolerated, considering the many benefits derived from electricity?

Electric utilities understandably find it desirable to use the ocean water for once-through cooling if the load centers are near the coast. But the coastlines are strongly desired for other uses, too. In California, the public wants the shoreline reserved for recreation and its natural beauty rather than for unsightly thermal power plants. There is a limit also to how much heat the coastal ocean can assimilate, although we are apparently still far from this limit in California.

When once-through cooling is not desirable, cooling ponds or evaporative cooling towers may be used. The use of cooling towers instead of once-through cooling systems increases the cost of electricity only about 1 to 2 percent for residential customers or 3 to 4 percent for industrial customers. But these systems also have their hydrologic impact, especially where water is scarce. In either case, most of the heat exchange to the atmosphere in warm weather occurs by evaporation of water from the pond surface or from the cooling–tower spray. For each kilowatt–hour of electricity generated, the evaporation is about 2 liters.

In the last few years large natural-draft cooling towers have come into use in the United States. When the circulating water is sprayed downward into the rising air current, a small fraction of the water (a few percent) is lost by evaporation and upward drift of droplets, necessitating a continuous inflow of makeup water to the system. Since such water usage is evaporative, the salts are left behind and have to be flushed out occasionally, thus degrading the quality of the remaining natural water supply. Dry (nonevaporative) cooling towers have not yet been developed for large power plants of hundreds or thousands of megawatts.

The waste-heat problem is not readily solved by technological change. Different outfall arrangements or siting alternatives can convert and distribute the heat in ways that minimize adverse effects, but the waste-heat discharges are not *eliminated.* Gradual small improvements in thermal efficiency of power plants will give barely perceptible relief on the waste-heat problem in the next few decades.

We shall continue to depend on large central power stations. One alternative, solar cells, has the advantage of using the present heat budget of the earth and circumvents the waste-heat problem (like hydro power), but the huge requirements for land and material will make it impractical for generation of the large blocks of additional power to meet projected needs in the next few decades.

The "globalists" would have us believe that we are far from environmental limits on energy use because man's energy input is small compared to the global heat budget. But they fail to allow for the fact that local and regional environmental impacts (such as in California or the northeastern United States) are rapidly becoming severe. Furthermore, heat dissipation is not the only problem; on all the other fronts as well (air pollution, mine debris, nuclear waste management, aesthetics), it is highly doubtful that technology can reduce the impact per unit of consumption at a continuing annual percentage rate anywhere near the current rate of growth of consumption. Each single technological improvement in environmental control is equivalent to only a one-time gain of a few years in an exponentially growing business; in some instances the improvement due to a new control technology may be counteracted by growth even faster than the new control technology can be implemented (as may well be the case for air pollution from automobiles).

Our most powerful tool for environmental control in the next few decades is a *drastic reduction in the rate of increase of consumption.* Society *must* set limits on the total release of heat and all other contaminants to protect the quality of our finite environment.

A decade ago energy planners were primarily concerned with the adequacy of our fuel reserves. But now nuclear power has proved itself, and with breeder reactors probably to be in use soon, there is little concern about running out of nuclear fuel. The next step will undoubtedly be fusion reactors using deuterium derived from a huge supply in the ocean waters. The great optimism on the fuel picture is well illustrated by a promotional booklet for nuclear energy entitled "Infinite Energy" issued by the Westinghouse Company a few years ago.

The "scarcity" of the environment is now replacing the scarcity of fuel as the critical constraint in growth of the energy industry. The environment can no longer be regarded as *infinite.* One hundred years ago it must have seemed to our forebears as though there was infinite land in the United States; but the frontier days are past, and we have become adjusted to thinking of our land as a scarce and limited resource. Any freedom to use land has been reduced by government regulations like zoning. We have also of course already recognized the finiteness of freshwater supplies, and have established rights, priorities, and regulations to control their use.

Now we have passed the last frontier of the infinite environment concept. We must stop talking about meeting the demand for energy and instead devise ways to allocate a limited potential supply and to change people's attitudes toward energy. The first step is to reduce the annual rate of increase—in a sense, to reverse the curvature of the growth curve. This does not imply an actual decrease of energy consumption but rather an attempt to level the growth curve off below some upper limit which is not too far above our current position.

Limiting the total growth of the energy usage is not a new idea, but somehow technologists always seem to concentrate just on reducing the adverse effects of each unit of usage, optimistically assuming that the overall growth will not overwhelm them. But the thought is beginning to appear in various reports. In its report *Elec-*

tric Power and the Environment (Aug. 1970), the Office of Science and Technology says: ". . . It may well be timely to re-examine all of the basic factors that shape the present rapid rate of energy growth in the light of our resource base and the impact of growth on the environment. We raise the issue here for further study and discussion."

I would have been happier if it said, "We raise the issue for action!"

A December 1969 report on energy forecasting for OST by Battelle Northwest slipped in just a one-sentence paragraph on the growth–environment issue: "It is even possible to envision Federal policies designed to slow the growth of energy consumption due to adverse environmental effects through rate-making policies and emphasis on increased efficiency."

It's not a question of whether it is "even possible"; it's a *necessity* to develop such policies if we want to survive this energy "explosion." It's not a case of saying the public is not ready for growth control. It's time for the technologists to say, "You must recognize the limitations of your environment and live within your environmental means."

The federal and state governments need to develop more comprehensive and better defined energy policies and strategies, such as the following:

1. All forms of energy must be considered together, so that comprehensive strategies involving tradeoffs between different fuels and energy systems can be adequately evaluated.

2. It must be recognized that energy usage must ultimately be limited because of unavoidable environmental effects (such as the release of heat). The attitude of unlimited development to meet unlimited demands must be replaced by a willingness to keep energy demands within reasonable limits, considering the limitations of the environment. Heat is an inevitable residual of industrial societies.

3. The growth rates must be drastically curtailed in the near future. This will not be easy, and a carefully developed strategy would probably include many of the following features:

a. The consumers of electricity and fuels should be charged for all environmental costs, including both direct costs for environmental pollution costs and indirect damages to the environment. Present pricing policies simply do not imply a high-enough value for the environment, which must be shared by all.

b. Regressive rate structures should be revised, as necessary, to discourage wasteful usage of energy by large users, who often enjoy preferential rates.

c. Stopping advertising and promotional programs, especially by electric utilities.

d. Establishment of taxes to increase the cost of energy use to discourage excessive usage.

e. Establishment of adequate licensing procedures and priorities for large new users of electricity or other energy sources. In some circumstances permits for use of energy should be denied where the environment cannot tolerate such additional energy uses.

f. Setting limits on unit consumption of energy by automobiles, electric appliances, houses, etc.

g. Discourage use of electricity as a simple source of heat, unless it is necessary for air-pollution control. Whenever one unit of electrical energy is used for heating, approximately two units of waste heat must be rejected to the environment; thus, even though electricity is a "clean" source of heat to the consumer, it loads more heat altogether into the environment.

h. In urban planning, limitations must be set for the areal density of total energy release in urban areas, in order to avoid excessive climatic change.

i. The consumer must learn not to use energy wastefully or carelessly, and realize that his consumption inevitably produces some environmental degradation.

4. A vigorous program of research and development on alternative long-range energy strategies should be undertaken. In a broadly interdisciplinary way, the new Environmental Quality Laboratory at Caltech, under the direction of Lester Lees, has already started a study of these problems.

5. More research is needed on the individual components of environmental control (e.g., air pollution, water pollution, radioactive wastes), and power-plant-siting alternatives (e.g., underground or underwater).

6. Establish adequate organizations to manage the environment in all aspects, with the ability to make tradeoffs between different kinds of environmental effects. (Should air pollution be solved in one place at the expense of a thermal-pollution problem somewhere else?)

7. Clarify environmental goals and damages, especially in the fields of medicine and ecology.

8. Energy systems and environmental limitations must become a central element in regional and urban planning.

9. Adequate long-range planning is vital, as illustrated by the electric power industry. Since the time required for licensing and construction of electric power plants is often 10 years, tentative site identification must be made 15 years before expected startup. The overall planning for a given utility must extend even further, say 20 years. Finally, basic policy planning for the whole energy industry must extend about 30 years into the future in order for orderly planning to proceed. It is because of this pattern that I sound the alarm for basic long-range questions of growth and other strategies rather than for any particular argument over a power-plant site.

Environmental control is the civilian counterpart of arms control. We now have the technology to do vast damage to our environment, even by the "normal" peacetime activities of society. We must accept some profound changes and restraints in our societies to control man's overall effects on the environment. The environment *is* definitely finite, and it simply can no longer tolerate man's unrestrained activities and new developments, whether of military or civilian nature.

JAMES J. MORGAN
*is professor of environmental
engineering science at Caltech. He
received his B.S. in civil
engineering at Manhattan College
and his M.S. degree in engineering
from the University of Michigan.
He taught at the University of
Illinois before going on to get his
Ph.D. at Harvard University in
1964 in water chemistry. His main
research interests are in the areas
of aquatic chemistry, water
treatment, and water-pollution
control. He is the editor of the
American Chemical Society journal*
Environmental Science and
Technology.

CHAIRMAN
Fred C. Anson
Professor of Analytical Chemistry
Caltech

JAMES J. MORGAN

Trace Metals
in the Environment

ANSON: The speaker today, Dr. James Morgan, Professor of Environmental Engineering Sciences at Caltech, was educated at Manhattan College, the University of Michigan, and Harvard. He's been at Caltech since 1965 and he's had an interesting background—some recent highlights include his assumption of the editorship of the ACS journal called *Environmental Science and Technology* and even more recently he has coauthored, with Werner Stumm, a new book called *Aquatic Chemistry*. Mr. Morgan.

MORGAN: I understand that this part of the series has to do with chemistry in society. I'd like to free you of any notion that what I want to give you is any heavy chemical burden of guilt. I think the popular journals and the newspapers and magazines will take care of that for you. This month's *Fortune* magazine has a very impressive piece on metals in the environment. The metals are characterized as "villains," but in my opinion the real villains are probably not the metals themselves—an interesting editorial twist that journalism has managed to insert into science. Or, as a student once remarked at Harvard, "Time permitting, we will be allowed to generate our own opinions."

I believe that the subject of trace metals in the environment is interesting and important and that chemists should take an active part in discussing this and related subjects. I would like to discuss some case histories and present some representative environmental data having to do with the elements lead and mercury. When we cooked up this assignment some time back I didn't realize that mercury would now be all that exciting, or at least that much in the public eye. But it is, because of the findings that mercury is present in many fish in amounts greater than that allowed by the FDA standard. Lead, on the other hand, has been the subject of some interest at Caltech for the past half-dozen years now, because of the geochemical research of Clair Patterson. That work—when he related it to environmental contamination by lead—brought him into a substantial confrontation with the traditional and generally accepted way of looking at things in public health and environmental medicine. That's a conflict which is still going on, and the resolution of it is not clear. Part of the difficulty is a question of physiological interpretation of certain environmental data. Also I must say that one thing I cannot talk about in very much depth is the physiological basis of lead or mercury toxicity.

One part of the problem we are considering is to understand how trace metals enter the environment, how they are transported and altered, and what sort of concentrations are achieved in different waters, regions, and living materials. The general idea is illustrated in the environmental "wheel" shown in Figure 1. The picture is adapted from a very interesting article by Professor Edward Deevey that appeared in the September 1970 issue of *Scientific American.* Deevey superimposed upon the lithosphere, hydrosphere, and atmosphere some features of the *biosphere.* The biosphere is defined as that part of the earth in which life exists (the "sphere" or domain of living things and their biochemical transfor-

Figure 1

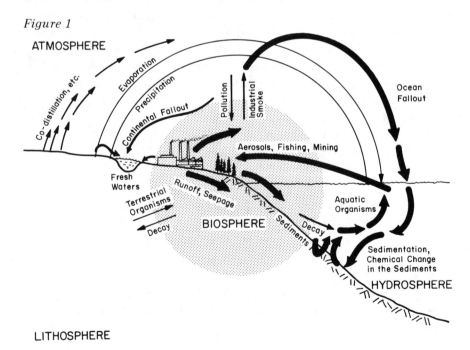

mations). The hydrosphere, or the water domains of the earth (71 percent of the earth's surface area); the lithosphere, or the domain of rocks; and the atmosphere, the gaseous envelope of the planet—together with the biosphere—constitute the four spheres through which chemicals move, whether naturally (geochemical weathering and the cycles of mobile elements) or through man's influences. The biosphere—to a very significant degree—interconnects the other three spheres. Deevey's purpose was to show what he felt was the "eutrophication" of the biosphere, by which he meant the *industrial* enrichment (by modern agriculture, industry, urbanization, etc.) of the biosphere, thus extending the notion of overfertilization beyond the simple introduction of phosphorus and nitrogen, extending it to all the agricultural and industrial activities carried out in our technological societies. I have added several nasty black arrows to Deevey's original illustration to show some of the ways in which contaminants—metal ions, for example, and the trace elements in general—can move through the "spheres." I hope, among other things, to suggest by this schematic view why straightforward analysis in looking for trace contaminants in obvious places (like water itself) is often not the most logical thing to do.

If you let the "factory" stand as a symbol for man's technological activities in general, you've got a fairly comprehensive routing scheme. You can route materials into the atmosphere, through industrial or domestic combustion processes; you can route them over the surface of the land or through rivers or through the ground waters; you can discharge them directly to the oceans in freshwater flows, as we do in southern California (albeit much modified by our extensive sewerage system, our storm water channels, and the fact of our intermittent rivers). Pollutants can later fall out directly on the land or on bodies of fresh water or on the oceans. They can "take off" from the land or from the water as vapors, aerosols, dust-blown particles, or co-distillates (as with DDT and water). Mercury, at least in small quantities, can enter the atmosphere as a vapor, in the elemental form and perhaps in other forms, such as the organic methyl mercury. Once in the marine environment or in fresh waters there are significant mechanisms for chemical change and concentration—in the plankton (free-floating microscopic plants and animals), the larger plants and animals, and in the sediments (both the living and the nonliving parts). These mechanisms involve a great deal of complex chemistry, most of which is not well understood. Mercury may enter the sediment as elemental Hg (lost, perhaps, from an industrial process) or as mercuric ion, Hg^{2+}, but it may escape from the sediments in a quite different form because of oxidation–reduction reactions or coordination reactions biologically mediated in the sediment environment. Aquatic organisms may take up an element upon its introduction in the water environment and concentrate it within their tissue. Once concentrated within an organism, the element can be moved and circulated through great distances (both horizontally and vertically).

Contaminant elements can return to the land from the oceans and lakes in a number of ways. Volatile elements and compounds can return simply by moving through the gas phase. Elements may be borne on aerocolloid particles formed at the sea surface and transported by the winds. Elements are returned to the land by mining of the seas. Biologically active elements are "captured" and returned to the land—at least temporarily—by fishing. That, in fact, is one of the reasons that mercury is so interesting right at the moment and why lead and other elements may be found to be just as interesting later. We do move many of the elements back to man in immense quantities. We do it with DDT and many other biologically concentrated elements and compounds. It's perhaps not realized to what a great extent we move materials just by fishing. The catch of fish is many tens of millions of tons each year. I did an exercise the other night after a drink (probably not the best time). I estimated the total pounds of people in the world and with the help of George Jackson I estimated the pounds of fish. It seems roughly that there are about as many pounds of fish as people. You can play some games about what would happen if the annual "loss" of mercury to the environment became lodged in either all the people or all the fish. And in fact, the rate of loss is large, and I don't think we should be so surprised to find large concentrations of mercury in some fish. What I'd like to suggest by these remarks is that the scale, the magnitude of the chemical *quantities* involved, is tremendous, even though the concentrations involved in some particular phases (for example, the water itself) may be quite small. Often we are taking on very tough analytical problems in measuring very small concentrations, but still the phenomena are global in every sense of the term.

The hydrosphere is mainly *oceans* (only 1 percent or so of the volume is fresh water and the greatest part of that is in the form of ice). The notion that the oceans are a *sink* is by now a familiar one. The oceans are, in fact, the natural repository for the end products of continental weathering. However, it is necessary to recognize—as I have implied in Figure 1—that the idea of an "ultimate sink" in the

Table 1

Human Activities and the Annual Cycle of Water

Element	A kg/yr mined	B kg/yr added to ocean	C kg/yr lost from ocean	Mined/ added to ocean	Mined/ lost from ocean
Ag	6.5×10^6	4.8×10^6	2×10^5	1.4	32
Al	1.1×10^{10}	8.9×10^9	1.4×10^{11}	1.2	0.08
As	2.7×10^6	1.5×10^7		0.18	
Au	10^6	$< 2 \times 10^6$	2.7×10^4	> 0.5	37
B	10^8	4.8×10^8	$2.5 \times 10^{7*}$	0.2	$4?$
Ba	1.5×10^9	2×10^9	5×10^8	0.75	3
Be	2.8×10^5	$< 4 \times 10^7$	5.6×10^6	> 0.007	0.05
Bi	1.4×10^6		6.2×10^5		2.2
Br	10^8	7.8×10^8	$3.5 \times 10^{8*}$	0.13	0.3
C	2×10^{12}	$> 3.9 \times 10^{11}$		< 5	
Ca	$5 \times 10^{11}?$	5.7×10^{11}	7×10^{10}	1	7
Cd	10^7	$< 3 \times 10^9$	3.1×10^5	> 0.003	32
Cl	5.3×10^{10}	2.9×10^{11}	10^{11*}	0.18	0.5
Co	1.5×10^7	3.3×10^7	2.1×10^7	0.45	0.7
Cr	2×10^9	6.7×10^6	2×10^8	300	10
Cu	4×10^9	3.7×10^8	8.4×10^7	11	50
F	8.3×10^8	3.3×10^9		0.25	
Fe	2.1×10^{11}	2.5×10^{10}	10^{11}	8	2
Ga	5×10^3	$< 4 \times 10^7$	3×10^7	> 0.0001	0.0002
Ge	8×10^4		1.4×10^7		0.06
H	1.8×10^9	4.1×10^{15}		0.000002	
Hg	10^7	3×10^6	10^6	3	10
I	2×10^6	7.4×10^8		0.003	
In	1.2×10^4				
K	8×10^9	8.5×10^{10}	4.8×10^{10}	0.1	0.17
La	$3 \times 10^5?$	3.7×10^7		0.008	
Li	2×10^6	4×10^7	1.2×10^7	0.05	0.17
Mg	1.2×10^8	1.5×10^{11}	4.2×10^{10}	0.0008	0.0025
Mn	6×10^9	4.4×10^8	2×10^9	14	3
Mo	3×10^7	1.3×10^7	2.8×10^7	2.3	1
N	1.7×10^{10}	$> 8.5 \times 10^9$	2.8×10^{11}	< 2	0.06
Na	3.1×10^{10}	2.3×10^{11}	5.7×10^{10}	0.13	0.5
Nb	2.5×10^5		4.7×10^7		0.005
Ni	3×10^8	3×10^8	4.2×10^8	1	0.7
O	10^{13}	3.3×10^{16}		0.0003	
P	1.4×10^9	1.8×10^8		8	
Pb	2.2×10^9	1.8×10^8	2.1×10^7	12	100
Pd	1.4×10^4				
Pt	1.4×10^4				
Rb	$9 \times 10^7?$	5.5×10^7		$1.6?$	
S	9×10^9	1.4×10^{11}		0.065	
Sb	4.5×10^7		1.3×10^6	35	
Se	9×10^5	$< 7 \times 10^8$		> 0.001	
Si	$3.8 \times 10^9?$	2.4×10^{11}	5.2×10^{11}	0.015	0.007
Sn	1.7×10^8	1.5×10^6	4.2×10^7	110	4
Sr	4.8×10^7	3×10^9	6×10^8	0.016	0.08
Ta	2.5×10^5		3.5×10^7		0.007
Te	2×10^5				
Ti	10^9	3.2×10^8	8.8×10^9	3	0.1
Tl	3×10^4		$54*$		600
U	3×10^7	3.7×10^7	8.4×10^6	0.8	4
V	8×10^6	3.7×10^7	2.8×10^8	0.2	0.03
W	3×10^7		1.4×10^8		0.2
Zn	3×10^9	3.7×10^8	7.8×10^7	8	40
Zr	1.3×10^6	9.6×10^7		0.014	

* Assuming a retention time in the ocean equal to that of sodium.

oceans can be misleading. There *are* feedback loops for a fraction of the flux of many elements. Furthermore, there are large differences in rates at which different elements and compounds find their way to the ocean sediments (the real "sink" if there is one). Where the rates of removal of an element from the oceans are slow, large rates of injection of an element lead to a buildup of the ocean concentration and to greater opportunities for recycling by various mechanisms (physical, biological). With these considerations in mind, let us turn our attention to some quantitative estimates for the fluxes of metals in the land–ocean system.

Estimated quantities of the elements added to the oceans by geochemical weathering and removed from the oceans by sedimentation are listed in Table 1. Also given are the annual rates of mining of elements. These data were gathered by Bowen in his valuable book on the trace elements. The quantity A is kilograms per year mined. For lead (Pb) the quantity is 2.2×10^9. The quantity B, kilograms per year added to the oceans, is the amount estimated to flow normally to the oceans in the rivers of the world. For Pb, that quantity is estimated at 1.8×10^8. Thus there is a sizable difference between the mining rate for lead and the geochemical flow to the oceans. The quantity C represents the annual amount estimated to be lost from the oceans by sedimentation. This represents geochemical estimate for the marine environment. The ratio A/C for lead turns out to be about 100. Bowen uses this sort of framework to identify elements of high *potential* pollution. It is a kind of diagnostic, although not a straightforward one. We are undoubtedly not in a steady state, and we don't know in detail where lead is accumulating on the continents and thus not reaching the ocean system. (A lot of lead from many years ago still resides in the paint of old city houses, to mention a familiar and regrettable example of accumulation of an element.) One of the largest uses of Pb is in tetraethyllead fuel additives, and we know that lead from that source ends up in the soil, in the rivers, in the atmosphere, in the oceans, and in people. One ought to look for lead just about everywhere.

What about mercury? Looking again at Table 1, we see 107 kg per year mined in the world and an estimated natural flux of 3×10^6 kg per year. [There appears to be much uncertainty in the quantity estimated for Hg weathering. E. D. Goldberg and D. Klein (*Environ. Sci. Technol.,* 4, 765, 1970) estimated 5×10^6 kg/yr for weathering. Others have recently placed the quantity at an order of magnitude smaller.] The rate of mining when compared with the ocean sedimentation rate indicates a tendency to accumulate in the

Table 2

Ocean, River, and Secondary Sewage Effluent Concentrations

Element	Concentrations, mg/l			Ratios	
	Ocean	River	Secondary effluent*	Effluent river	Effluent ocean
Cr	0.00005	0.00018	0.11	610	2200
Pb	0.00003	0.005	0.03	6	1000
Fe	0.01	0.67	0.37	0.55	37
P	0.07	0.005	6.6	1320	94
N	0.5	0.23	12.0	52	24
Cu	0.003	0.01	0.16	16	53
Ni	0.0054	0.01	0.12	12	22
Zn	0.01	0.01	0.20	20	20
Al	0.01	0.24	0.28	1.2	28
Mn	0.002	0.012	0.06	5	30
As	0.003	0.0004	0.02	50	7
Se	0.00009	0.02	0.03	1.5	333
Si	3	6.5	9	1.4	3
B	4.6	0.013	0.86	6.6	0.2
Inorganic carbon.	28	11	55	5	2
Organic carbon	0.5	2	5	2.5	10

*Data from Norman H. Brooks, Some Data on Municipal Waste Discharges to the Pacific Ocean in the Los Angeles Area, unpublished report, 1969. Data given are for secondary effluent from Hyperion sewage treatment plant, City of Los Angeles, in 1966.

ocean waters or the biota. Another metal in Table 1 which I've underlined for emphasis is cadmium. Even in the absence of any detailed biological evidence, we ought to be looking hard at cadmium in the environment. The rate of mining cadmium is on the same order as that of mercury. The chemical characteristics of cadmium, its tendency to complex in the divalent state, and its tendency to associate with organic substances (possibly playing the same sort of biochemical roles as divalent Hg) are all of interest. In comparing the rate of industrial generation of cadmium with the weathering rate—the rate is 32—one can identify a tendency to some accumulation.

To get some feeling for the situation in southern California coastal waters I'd like to show some data which were compiled recently by Professor Norman Brooks of Caltech, from information available in the Los Angeles area (Table 2). We can look at a group of elements: chromium, lead, iron, and also copper, nickel, zinc, aluminum, manganese, arsenic, and selenium. These are some of the trace metals. We know something about their concentrations in seawater and in the rivers of the world. The numbers in the third column of Table 2 are estimates of the concentrations in the primary (basically, following settling basins) effluents of sewage-treatment plants. If we take the ratio of the effluent and ocean concentrations, we notice that for chromium the value is 2200. Thus chromium is evidentally enriched in coastal waters, or in coastal sediments. For lead, the ratio of effluent to ocean concentrations is about 1000. Unfortunately, there are some important elements missing from this table. Data should be obtained for mercury, for example. It has been repeated over and over again in the articles I've been reading for the last several months that we don't have nearly enough information on trace elements in the environment; that's a fairly accurate assessment.

If spread uniformly throughout the waters of the oceans, the metal concentrations in waste effluents might not concern us so much. But local concentrations in food chains within the biosphere are another matter. Table 3 contains some data on concentration factors of elements in marine organisms. Concentrations of an element in seawater are compared with concentrations in different biological materials. For example, the concentration of Pb in anchovy is about 10,000 times greater than the concentration in seawater. For zinc the concentration ratio in seaweed is about 900; for manganese in one group of marine animals the ratio ranges from 2000 to 10,000. Although the numbers are not known accurately, the concentration factors for *some* elements and *some* organisms can be

Table 3

Concentration Factors of Elements in Marine Organisms

Organisms	Cu	Ni	Pb	Co	Zn	Mn	Mg	Ca	Sr	Ba
Seaweeds (Black and Mitchell, 1952)	—	550	—	—	900	—	—	—	23	—
Benthic algae		2000–				1000–				
(Lowman, 1964)	—	40,000	—	—	—	30,000	—	—	—	—
Plankton (Nicholls et al., 1960)	400–	<20–	30–	<100						
	90,000	8000	12,000	16,000	—	—	—	—	—	—
Marine animals		3000–				2000–				
(F. G. Lowan, Personal Communication)	—	70,000	—	—	—	10,000	—	—	—	—
Anchovetta (Goldberg, 1962)	80	—	10,000	—	400	1000	0.1	7	8	20
Yellow fin tuna (Goldberg, 1962)	200	—	—	—	700	80	0.2	6	7	2
Skipjack tuna (Goldberg, 1962)	100	50	—	—	500	40	0.3	5	5	3
Sponges (Bowen and Sutton, 1951)	1400	420	—	50	—	—	—	0.07	3.5	—

† E. D. Goldberg, in *Chemical Oceanography*, J. P. Riley and G. Skirrow, Eds., Academic Press, New York, 1965, p. 185. The only inter-comparisons that are valid are along horizontal lines (different techniques were used for different organisms). The elements are arranged in the "Irving-Williams" order to illustrate the relation between concentration factors and complex stability.

quite large. It is clear that this phenomenon represents an important mechanism for concentrating an element as it moves up a food chain in the biosphere. This is now well known for DDT and is also true for many of the trace metal ions. The simple organisms achieve a certain concentration ratio with respect to the water. These organisms are eaten by predators, which may achieve a still larger concentration ratio. At perhaps the third, fourth, or fifth level of a food chain (or branch on a food web) the concentration factors may be like those shown for the animals in Table 3. The analytical implications are very significant. In order to understand the environmental chemistry of a trace metal one generally should not look just in the water—that very often turns out to be the wrong place to look. The *right* place to look would be in the key participants in the food chains.

I'd like to give you a feeling for the sort of reasoning that we ought to go through to get a notion about the environmental impact of an element. Suppose we take a look at mercury. Goldberg estimates that the annual world production is about 9200 tons. Bowen has estimated that its 10^7 kg/yr—those numbers are fairly close. If we look at quantities of mercury produced, imported, used, and inventoried we note a discrepancy—mercury is "lost" or unaccounted for somehow. Data on this sort of thing are given, for example, in the November 1970 issue of *Environmental Science and Technology.* The average annual discrepancy of mercury, that is, mercury unaccounted for on the national balance sheet, for the years 1945 through 1958 was 2 million pounds. I get the feeling that if we "integrate" back over the preceding 30 or 40 years we conclude that a very large total mass of mercury has gone into various parts of the soil, air, fresh water, and marine environments. Simple-mindedly, if we apportion the average annual discrepancy for mercury to the tonnage of fish in the world oceans, we get a surprisingly large average concentration. That's not a very scientific thing to do, of course, but it gives one some feeling for the problem we seem to be discovering just now. One might ask: Should I be surprised if I find that some fish in the world are showing mercury concentrations on the order of 5 to 10 ppm? I think the answer is no. The large quantities and the wide dispersion are a part of what we mean by a "global" problem of environmental contamination.

Referring back to Table 3, because of the selectivity of certain organisms, some are going to have quite high concentrations of mercury (and other elements) while other organisms can be expected to have much lower concentrations. There are wide variations in the hydrologic, chemical, and biological processes all over the world which yield such wide variations in biotic concentrations. However, we should not be surprised to see that nearly all rivers, ocean waters, sediments, and organisms are showing up "large" concentrations of mercury. The "lost" mercury must go somewhere. This fact has policy implications for all trace metals.

I'll try now to use the case of lead to illustrate some other factors involved with the trace metal in the environment. Lead is largely emitted into the air. Lead comes out of the automobile exhaust in particulate form, as a mixture of lead halides and oxides, probably predominantly the chlorides and the bromides of Pb(II). The lead emerges as particles with sizes ranging from about 1 to 10 microns. (A micron is 10,000 angstroms, or, in those old-fashioned dimensions, about 1/25,000 of an inch.) Larger lead-containing particles deposit at locations closer to the roadway; smaller particles are transported to much greater distances. The lead is then incorporated into the soil system by processes of sedimentation, dissolution, and ionic movement, either as the simple ion or as an inorganic (carbonate, sulfate, hydroxo) or organic complex species. It would also be desirable to distinguish between oxidized, Pb(IV), lead and reduced, Pb(II), lead in environmental samples; the chemical and biological implications of the difference appear to be significant. Unfortunately, the analytical distinction has not yet been made.

One of the recent controversies concerning lead has to do with its fate in the soil. Does it get taken up readily into the plant system? Or is the major path for getting "excess" lead into the plant system one starting with deposition of particles on the leaves? A series of papers dealing with environmental lead, published in *Environmental Science and Technology* in March 1970, suggests that deposition on the leaves is probably the dominant mechanism for getting the lead into or onto the plants and that the route through the soil system is a slow one. The fact that lead is initially in a particulate form is important to recognize in considering the analytical chemistry of environmental lead as well as the modes by which it moves through the atmosphere, hydrosphere, and biosphere.

An example of airborne lead distribution in a city is shown in Figure 2. These are data obtained about 4 years ago in the Chicago area. Shown are lead concentrations in micrograms per cubic meter. Notice the Eisenhower Expressway—heavily traveled—with a concentration of about 3. Away from the downtown area, concentrations of about a few tenths are typical. These data were obtained by filtration and atomic absorption spectrophotometry. The sort of picture shown in Figure 2 is more or less typical for U.S. metropolitan

Figure 2

Lead concentrations (microgram per cubic meter) samples in Cook County, Ill., on March 31, 1966

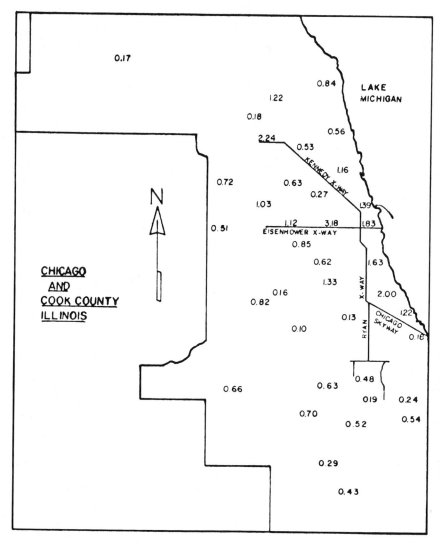

centers. Lead is present in urban air largely as particles and it is strongly correlated with heavy traffic.

As you might expect, lead concentrations in surface air are accentuated in urban areas on a global basis. In following the meridian that goes through New York City, one observes concentrations in the air like those shown in Table 4, for 1967. Up north, the concentrations are less than 0.01 microgram per cubic meter. There

Table 4

Lead Concentrations in Surface Air (1967)

	Latitude	μg. per m.^{3}
Thule	70° N	<0.01
Moosonee	56° N	0.06
New York	41° N	2.5
Sterling, Va.	39° N	0.74
Miami	26° N	1.7
Bimini	26° N	0.10
San Juan	18° N	0.80
Balboa	9° N	0.23
Guayaquil	2° S	0.35
Lima	12° S	0.50
Chacaltaya	16° S	0.09
Antofagasta	24° S	0.06
Santiago	33° S	0.87
Punta Arenas	53° S	0.06

Figure 3

Lead values averaged from September 1966 to March 1967. Plotted numerals are g./ha./mo. Symbols are g./ha./cm. of precipitation

  ● 0–0.4   ■ 0.5–0.9   ◆ 1–4   ▲ 5–9   ○ 10–14
  ▲ 15–

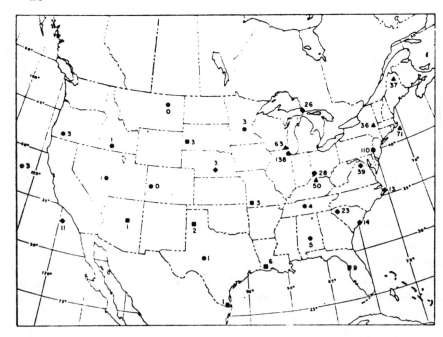

is a strong peak at New York City, with additional urban peaks at Miami, San Juan, and Santiago.

James P. Lodge and his co-workers at the National Center for Atmospheric Research at Boulder, Colorado, have investigated atmospheric lead in a different manner (Figure 3). They've looked at concentrations of lead in the rain. Figure 3 shows grams of lead per hectare per month in the precipitation at different locations in the United States. In the southern California area we see a rainfall lead flux on the order of 11 grams per hectare per month. Philadelphia and the Wilmington, Delaware, area show a value of about 100. Lodge correlated these environmental lead data with the 1966 sales

Figure 4

The dependence of lead on gasoline consumption plotted, or average gram of lead deposited on one hectare by one centimeter of precipitation vs. sales of gasoline in the locale of the collecting station in thousands of dollars. (The numbers in parentheses identify the station location.)

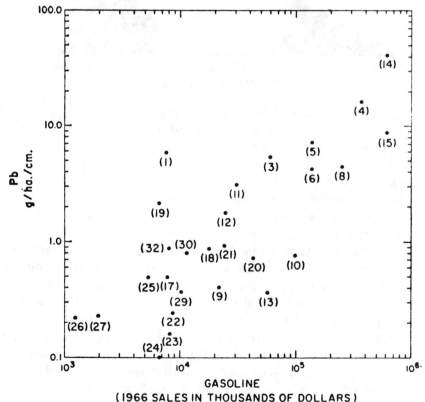

Figure 5

Frequency distribution of sample population by blood lead, sex, and residence; Los Angeles County, 1966.

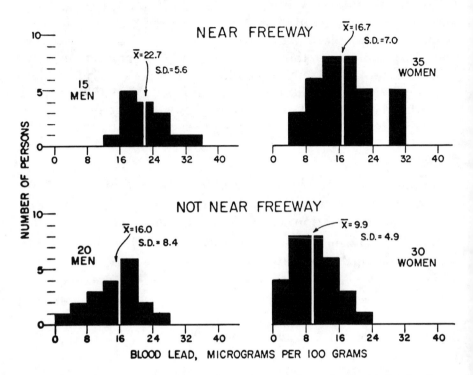

of gasoline (Figure 4). That's bringing it all back home! I doubt that anyone argues these days that airborne lead does *not* come from automobile exhausts in substantial amounts. There is, however, a great deal of discussion about what such data mean in human terms. (There is also the matter of whether lead in gasoline prevents effective control of other pollutants from automotive exhausts.)

A final illustration of lead concentrations in the environment—this time for humans—brings the case even closer to home (Figure 5). What sort of human blood levels for lead do you find near and far away from the Los Angeles freeways? Shown are distributions of blood lead levels (micrograms per 100 grams of blood) for men and women. If you examine the distributions you see that for women near the freeways there was a mean blood lead of 16.7; away from the freeway there was a mean of about 9.9. For men, the corresponding values were 22.7 and 16.0. Many such data are available now showing the kind of blood lead levels that are experienced by people in different geographic situations as well as in different occupa-

Table 5

Stable Lead in New York City Diet (1966 Sampling)

Diet category	kg./year	mg. Pb/kg.	mg. Pb/year
Dairy products	200	0.04	8
Fresh vegetables	48	0.12	6
Canned vegetables	22	0.44	10
Root vegetables	10	0.07	1
Potatoes	38	0.17	6
Dried beans	3	0.02	...
Fresh fruit	59	0.07	4
Canned fruit	11	0.25	3
Fruit juices	28	0.09	3
Bakery products	44	0.39	17
Flour	34	0.04	1
Whole grain products	11	0.13	1
Macaroni	3	0.08	...
Rice	3	0.04	...
Meat	79	0.42	33
Poultry	20	0.30	6
Eggs	15	0.22	3
Fresh fish	8	0.16	1
Shellfish	1	0.31	...
Total annual intake			103

tions. As you might expect, occupation and industrial setting have quite a lot to do with the levels observed.

A point which I think is of great importance in this whole business of trace contaminants and trace metals and their environmental significance for humans is that the total input to man comes from a variety of sources. One is through the air we breathe, another is through the water we drink, and a third is through our diet. You can get an impression about the relative sources of lead, for example, if you consider the concentrations in the air and the concentrations that are now found in water. At the present time it turns out that the important source of lead intake for man is the food he eats. The data in Table 5 are from a paper by Harley for a 1966 sampling of stable lead in the New York City diet. An estimated annual intake on the order of 100 mg of lead per year in the New York City diet is arrived at. Harley has also estimated the annual air intake of lead at about 15 mg and that from drinking at about 5 mg of lead. Thus

Figure 6

Barium and lead concentrations in sea waters as a function of depth. (*a*) Barium typifies many metals with increased contents at depth, most probably as a result of a transfer by plants and animals. (*b*) The source of the high lead in surface waters is attributed to the combustion of gasoline, containing tetraethyllead, in automobile engines. (T. J. Chow and C. C. Patterson, Concentration profiles of barium and lead in Atlantic waters off Bermuda, Earth Planet. Sci. Lett., 1:397–400, 1966).

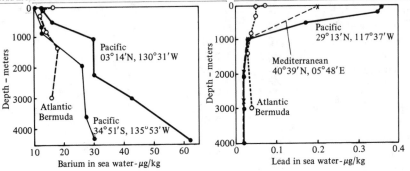

the dominant influence on the lead in an urban area is almost certainly the diet, the next influence in magnitude would be the air, the the third influence would be the drinking water. That sort of pattern can change with time.

The last part of my story about lead is borrowed from Patterson and Chow's work and it shows the way that the urban inputs of lead we've been talking about are reflected in the concentrations of lead in seawater (Figure 6). In the Pacific, the Mediterranean, and the Atlantic the pattern of lead concentration versus depth is the same. The concentrations in the surface waters have built up to considerably higher levels than must have existed before. But, on the other hand, barium, which behaves roughly like lead in terms of its biological concentration, shows very low concentrations in the surface waters and high concentrations in the deep waters. It is being transported largely by biological concentration phenomena and is not accumulating as a result of a high rate of industrial injection in the surface waters. Lead, which is also biologically concentrated, is, however, accumulating in the surface waters apparently because of the high rate of injection. The ocean mixing time is on the order of 500 to 1000 years for the Pacific. You can imagine that something that's been undergoing an increased injection on a time scale of 30 or 40 years would be expected to be quite concentrated only in the surface waters and to be greatly changed in deeper waters. That's the kind of picture you get by looking at the lead data for the oceans. The surface concentration, according to Patterson's estimate, is on the order of 10 to 30 times higher than the concentrations that ex-

Figure 7

Production of acetaldehyde at Minamata factory and the number of cases of Minamata disease between 1952 and 1960. (*K. Irukayama, The pollution of Minamata Bay and Minimata disease, Advan. Water Pollut. Res., 3:153–180, 1967*)

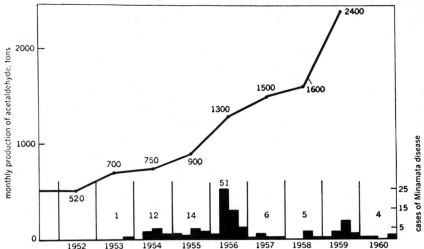

isted in the ocean sometime before the industrial revolution and before the use of tetraethyllead. The implications of this are again not obvious, but it probably means that many plants and animals in the ocean as well as man on the land have higher concentrations of lead than before. At the very least it means that the ocean waters have higher concentrations and that there is a reservoir of lead accumulation in essentially all the ocean waters of the world.

We have grown accustomed to talking about environmental density in terms of the *elements* themselves. The case of mercury in the environment—in the biosphere in particular—points up the importance of knowing more than simply how much of an element is present. It turns out to be important to know the *forms.* The case of Minamata disease is illustrative of the point. In 1953 a severe neurological disorder was recognized among inhabitants in the vicinity of Minamata Bay in south Kyushu, Japan (Figure 7). By 1960, 111 cases had been reported, most ending fatally or with permanent severe disability. Among the symptoms associated with the disease were fits, tremors, unsteady movements, and blindness. All victims had eaten either fish or shellfish from Minamata Bay. According to Japanese scientists (see, for example, K. Irukayama, The Pollution of Minamata Bay and Minamata Disease, *Advan. Water Pollut. Res., 3,* 153, 1967) abundant mercury had been accumulating in the muds at the bottom of the bay, but no organic mercury compound was identified in these muds. It was established—by chemical analyses and epidemiological work—that the source of the organic mercury which concentrated in the fish and shellfish and was taken up by the victims of the "disease" was the acidic wastewater from an acetaldehyde factory located on the bay. The organomercury compound extracted from the acetaldehyde plant sludge was proved to be CH_3HgCl, methyl mercury chloride. This compound, administered to cats, induced the various symptoms of the disease. Treatment facilities to control mercury discharge from the plant were installed in 1960. Since that time the mercury content of fish and shellfish in Minamata Bay has been reported decreasing. In 1965, a second outbreak of Minamata disease occurred—but far from Minamata Bay. It took place at Niigata City. There, 26 cases and 5 deaths were reported. Methyl mercury compounds, this time originating in the spent catalyst of an autoldehyde factory, were again responsible.

The history of Minamata disease has an important lesson: that the form in which a trace metal enters the biosphere may be decisive for its uptake, retention, and transmission to higher animals and man. Echoes of Minamata disease sounded in the recent case of mercury poisoning of three children of a family in Alamogordo, New Mexico. The Huckleby family children had consumed pork from a home-butchered hog highly contaminated with a methyl mercury fungicide, Panogen (a cyano methyl mercury guanidine). The hog was one of a number that had been fed over a period of many weeks with grain that had been previously treated with the fungicide. An excellent account of the Alamogordo incident appeared in *The New Yorker* magazine (another "scientific" journal which you're probably reading more and more chemistry these days) this past fall (1970).

So, in fact, what was called Minamata "disease" is a case of poisoning by the trace metal mercury through the food chain. But the specific *form* of methyl mercury turns out to be the potent chemical entity. This is something that demonstrates the great need for chemical insight in grappling with environmental hazards. We could use more techniques for identifying and naming of particular species. In looking at the literature it's often very difficult to find out what's going on with mercury in the environment. The form in which it's being discharged often is not even known. It's difficult to understand the rates and the mechanism of its transformations in the environment. Certain forms of mercury are innocuous when discharged but may become quite potent after they have undergone

Figure 8

Environmental increases in mercury levels as record-ed in the feathers of the eagle owl (*Bubo bubo*) collected from Sweden over the past 130 years. The increase in mercury in the 1940s and 1950s corresponds to increased usages of mercury alkyl compounds as seed dressings to combat fungal growths. The seeds were presumably ingested by the birds.

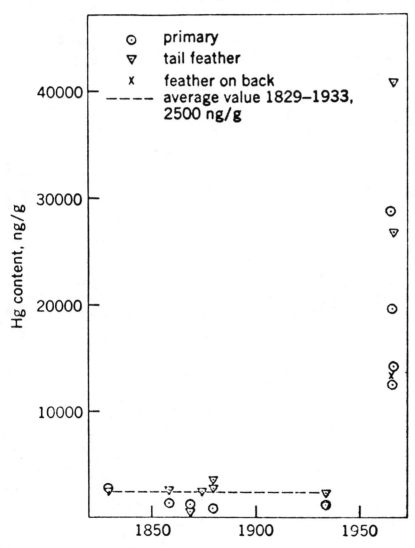

chemical changes in, for example, the muds of a lake.

Another example of the importance of the chemical form of mercury is the experience in Sweden with environmental contamination. Figure 8 depicts mercury content of the eagle owl *(Bubo bubo)* in Sweden during the nineteenth and twentieth centuries. Environmental scientists in Sweden have looked recently at the museum specimens of the birds over 130 years and made analyses

Figure 9

Mercury concentrations in parts per million on a dried weight basis in surface sediment samples near the Hyperion sewer outfall, Los Angeles

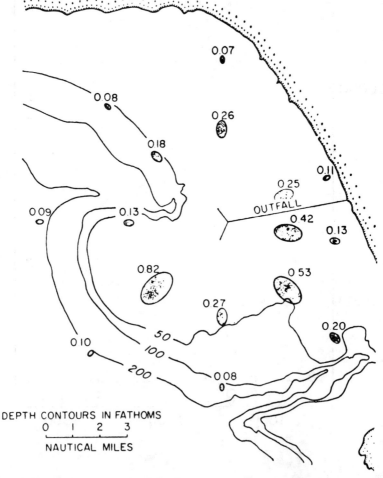

The ellipse area is a measure of the mercury concentration

of the mercury content of the feathers. The levels were quite low until between 1940 and 1950, when there was a big jump, corresponding to increased usage of mercury alkyl compounds, in place of the phenyl or inorganic compounds that had been used before. Methyl mercury is a much more mobile form than the simple Hg ion form or the phenyl mercury form. This is shown dramatically in the particular case of the accumulated mercury in the birds paralleled by the increase in deaths of birds. The trend has been reversed by a decision to go back to forms of mercury other than the methyl form as an agricultural chemical and a seed dressing. The accumulation tendency has been reduced and the excessive fatalities of large numbers in the bird population have been halted. The Swedish workers have been digging very deeply into the environmental den-

Figure 10

Mercury concentrations (in parentheses) in parts per million by weight on dried weight basis in surface sediment samples from the environs of the White Point sewer outfalls

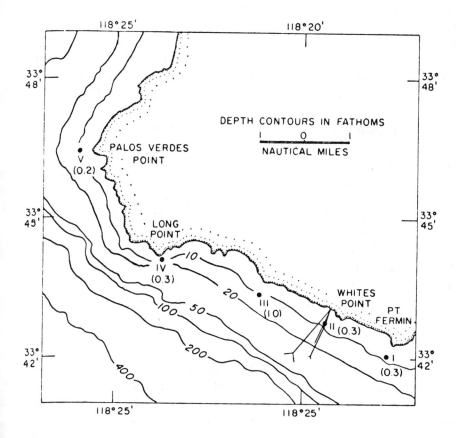

sity of mercury. The United States, Canada, Japan, and Sweden seem to have been the countries that have been most noticeably affected by mercury distribution in the environment over the last 10 years. Now we are experiencing a great spurt of chemical and biological interest in the origins, transformation, and ultimate fate (if such there be) of environmental mercury. Among the interesting chemical questions are: How does one identify and quantify different mercury species? What are the processes by which elemental and ionic forms are converted to organic forms in the environment? And what are the rates of movement and uptake of the different forms in the waters, the sediments, and the biota?

To demonstrate the effect close by, mercury is now accumulating in Los Angeles waters. Figure 9, from a September 1970 paper on mercury in the marine environment by Klein and Goldberg of the Scripps Institution of Oceanography, shows data on the Hg content of marine sediments near the Hyperion sewage effluent of the City of Los Angeles on Santa Monica Bay. Sediment concentrations on the order of 1/2 to 3/4 ppm (by weight) are noted in the vicinity of the outfall. Farther from the outfall discharge sediment, mercury levels are lower. Figure 10, from the same authors, shows similar data for the vicinity of the County of Los Angeles sewage outfall at Whites Point, east of the Palos Verdes area. Unfortunately, I don't know of many data on the mercury content of the sewage effluent—it was not routinely determined, apparently, before the present awareness of mercury's environmental significance. The mercury content of the liquid effluent (subject to primary treatment or partial secondary treatment) is perhaps up to a few parts per billion (or micrograms per liter). Evidently, concentration of mercury is taking place in the sediment in the vicinity of the Los Angeles area outfalls.

Table 6 shows the mercury data of Klein and Goldberg for bottom sediments and marine organisms at La Jolla and at five stations in the Palos Verdes area. These are not very extensive data, but they are sufficient to show biological concentration of mercury by the animals with respect to the seawater concentrations. It's not too surprising, then, to find evidence elsewhere that mercury can accumulate to high levels in other marine fauna. Remember that the Pure Food and Drug Administration standard maximum for swordfish is 0.5 ppm.

There's not yet very much known about mercury in the air but Figure 11 is an example of the little bit that is known. A study was done in the area between San Francisco and San Jose. The levels were monitored on a day with fresh southwest winds, that is, predominently air coming in from over the ocean and having a fairly low content of mercury. These data were compared with levels measured on a smoggy day. Some fantastically sharp peaks show up at about the time of the day when you would expect photochemical smog and industrial activity to be picking up in an area like San Francisco, but I don't think the chemical implications are at all clear. One thing that is certain is the change between a day with west-southwest wind and a day with reverse winds and smog. From the general chemical characteristics of mercury you might expect it to be able to move through the air in smaller concentrations than occur in water or in the biota. It would be interesting to know more about the physical and chemical forms of atmospheric mercury.

Let me try to summarize briefly. The subject of trace metals in the environment is more or less exemplary for the whole field of environmental chemistry, particularly for illustrating the global, widespread character of the problems. The key elements are emission sources (with the possibilities for control), dispersion in the environment (the land, the hydrosphere, the atmosphere, and the biosphere), detection in the environment, and the effects on living things—from the lower forms of life through human populations. It is necessary to identify the distribution and magnitudes of emission sources and to devise methods of control. It is pertinent to compare the emission levels from human activities with natural geological processes. It is essential to understand the pathways of dispersion and chemical–biological changes (recognizing that the environment may not simply "biodegrade," it may synthesize new chemical forms and recycle and concentrate substances to higher levels).

Table 6

Mercury Concentrations in Bottom Sediments and Organisms, Collected Off La Jolla and Palos Verdes (PV)[a]

Sample	Station					
	La Jolla	PV(I)	PV(II)	PV(III)	PV(IV)	PV(V)
Sediment	0.02	0.3	0.2	1.0	0.3	0.2
Crab, *Cancer*	0.8	1.0	1.2	0.5	2.3	
anthonyi		1.1			0.9	
Whelk, *Kelletia*	1.5	0.9	1.8	2.3	1.6	3.2
kelletia	0.9			1.6	2.5	
	2.1					
Rock scallop,	0.7	1.0	0.4			0.5
Hinnites	1.6	0.6				
multirugosus						

[a] p.p.m., dry wt. basis.

I have tried to give you a feeling for some of the environmental chemical characteristics of lead and some of the corresponding characteristics of mercury. I have broadly indicated what sort of scientific, economic, and technological factors are involved, and what sort of general biological factors are operative. I have not discussed the physiological bases. There are a few literature refer-

Figure 11

Mercury concentrations in air collected in San Francisco area. (a) Levels on day with fresh southwest winds. (b) Readings on smoggy day. (S. H. Williston, Mercury in the atmosphere, J. Geophys Res, 73 7051 – 7055, 1968)

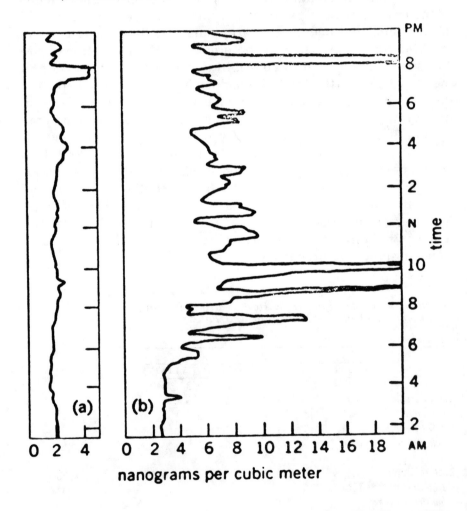

nanograms per cubic meter

ences that develop the basic biochemical ideas. The basic biochemical idea underlying the biological behavior of mercury, for example, is its very strong affinity for the sulfur-containing groups. Second, is the affinity of *organic* mercury for certain tissue. The competition between methyl mercury as a metal ion for various ligands in the living system seems to be able to account for the general patterns of mobility. Where we find mercury in the blood, in which organs of the body, and its ability to move through membranes—these factors seem to be associated with its presence as methyl mercury.

And so with that I end my own presentation and turn the discussion back to Fred Anson.

/ Discussion /

ANSON: Thank you Jim, I'm sure you've raised a lot of reactions and questions in people's minds, I had a couple but would prefer to solicit comments or questions from the audience.

QUESTION: Have there been any studies done on the effects of these pollutants in the ocean since we had that significant decrease in fish-catches intake in the past 2 years?

MORGAN: There was a seminar in our environmental engineering science group a couple of weeks ago—it didn't have to do with lead and mercury—it had to do with zinc and copper and a situation in Nova Scotia. Steve Dennis reviewed some fairly convincing recent evidence that coastal pollution by these two metal ions was having a significant effect upon the number of successful returns of fish to the spawning ground, and thus affecting spawning success. The kind of effort that is required to document cases of marine pollution is not small. In looking at the literature there are too few studies of this sort.

QUESTION: The problems with the detection of trace metals in the environment are coming at the same time at which Caltech and many other schools have almost completely removed from their curricula any traces of what you would call analytical chemistry. What are the principal analytical techniques that are being used to detect mercury and lead in the various environmental forms?

MORGAN: The principal analytical techniques for mercury are atomic absorption spectrophotometry, neutron activation analysis, and emission spectroscopy. Almost all the data that I've shown here from various investigators have been taken by one of those three methods.

QUESTION: How high are the mercury levels in the fish that were impounded:

MORGAN: They were sometimes as high as 20 ppm. They ranged from about 1 to 20 ppm in those cases where they have been measured.

QUESTION: Do the analytical methods still have to be worked out?

MORGAN: Oh, no, there are standard methods now for nearly all these things, but I think it's fair to say that many of the standard methods are still subject to considerable revision and improvement. Air methods are perhaps more extensive and critically reviewed right now than the water methods. There are standard methods for examinations of water and biological materials and methods for the analysis of the air. The standard methods textbook for water is revised about every 6 or 7 years. New principles and new methods of analysis are needed, particularly for species differentiation. Would you want to comment on that, Bill?

FROM AUDIENCE: Yes, I wanted to make a separate comment in that most of the people who make these measurements quote techniques and standardizations. But after it's sifted through from the original publication to secondary things and finally into the newspapers there's never any indication that there is any uncertainty. It is most distressing to see that. Second, I think what Fred Anson's after is the fact that the official government method for the analysis of mercury is antiquated; if any one of you tries to do it, lots of luck.

QUESTION: I was wondering whether the concentrations of mercury in the food chain are confined to coastal areas or are found throughout the ocean.

MORGAN: My understanding is that most of the ocean is relatively a biological desert in the sense that the large concentrations of plants and animals are in the areas of upwelling or near the coasts where nutrients flow in. (Areas of upwelling are regions where there's a great nutrient enrichment through certain ocean current configurations. Very high fish yields are found in such areas.) So I don't expect to find food-chain concentration phenomena universally. I'd expect food-chain enrichments in upwelling regions and in rich coastal areas, like some of those near our California metropolitan areas.

QUESTION: Los Angeles dumps its waste in the ocean—lots of big cities do this. Do we have any experience with large cities that don't have waterways available as to what they do with their waste?

MORGAN: What would be an example of a large city that doesn't have waterways?

QUESTION: Well, you can take a city like Calcutta, which doesn't have any sewage system at all. Should we discontinue discharging municipal wastes to the ocean?

MORGAN: In my opinion, no. After all, we know pretty well how many pounds of organic matter per day or per year is wasted by the 9 or 10 million people that live in the metropolitan area of southern California. That material must either accumulate on the land, be combusted into the atmosphere, or introduced as efficiently as possible into the biogeochemical cycles that operate in the ocean. I think the scientific and engineering job is to understand where in the system you can harmlessly introduce that material. There's no alternative to introducing it into the environment, for, after all, just setting it on the ground is a form of introducing it into the "environment."

I think we we need to know an awful lot more about the metabolic rates of different parts of the biosphere, different ecological "compartments," if you will. If you look at the total carbon that's involved in human metabolism every year, it's a small amount compared to the carbon metabolism of the forest systems and the biological systems in the ocean. The disturbances come when we introduce very large concentrations of organic matter into *small* systems like the East River or the Harlem River or Los Angeles Harbor without any attention to the fact that they're too concentrated.

I think one of the things we've learned from looking at mercury and lead and related things, though, is that it's not just the human waste that is the problem. We have to argue more and more for complete segregation of certain types of industrial waste. There have been economic advantages in the past in mixing up human waste with industrial waste—advantages of scale in handling, for example. Now, I think, we have to take a second look and realize that sometimes this mixing of carbonaceous wastes and trace element wastes is exactly what we don't want. The chlorine alkali plants in the United States and Canada are going to have to exert much more rigorous control on their mercury. Recycling is one of the best ways to control it. But if you have to *control* without recycling, then I think it must still be done. Mercury just cannot be turned loose.

"Recycling" is a kind of slogan of the new ecological movement. It may turn out, even on ecological grounds, that recycling may not be the best thing to do in all cases for all elements and compounds. It may turn out that you do not want to recycle some things back to the land completely because some of the natural flow really ought to go to the ocean. But you have to look very closely at what ought to go to the ocean, what can go to the lake, and what should be locked on the land.

QUESTION: Is it correct to think that mercury as the metal is less harmful?

MORGAN: Yes. The Swedes have observed in general that when they discharge mercury as such or mercuric mercury the effects are not nearly as harmful as for organic mercury compounds. However, they also observed that the environment has learned the trick for methylating the mercury. Apparently in the deoxygenated sludges methane-forming bacteria can methylate a mercuric salt and produce mono- and dimethyl mercury. Then it becomes a mobile substance that can escape into the water. The mercury we put out in an innocuous form got transformed into a more dangerous form.

QUESTION: Why was there no correlation between the deaths from Minamata disease and the production of acetaldehyde?

MORGAN: This was a kind of sporadic history. They were aware over the years that something was going on. It's really a stochastic sort of picture which also has to do with the annual seasonal variation of the fish catch and how much organic mercury gets into the food chain. Also I suspect that the water discharge was not a steady day-by-day discharge but a series of accidental spills or unrecognized leaching from the land into the bay waters.

QUESTION: The FDA two months ago suggested that no pregnant woman in California should ingest a fish caught by noncommercial fisheries in northern California because the mercury content was so high it could give brain damage to the fetus. Can you suggest on this basis that we might have the problem of mercury poisoning in the United States?

MORGAN: Yes. That statement is safe enough for me to agree with it.

QUESTION: Is there a mercury level known to cause poisoning in man?

MORGAN: Yes, there is information on the toxic mercury level. As you might expect, it varies with the organ—liver, kidney, brain, plasma —the concentrations would range over numbers like 10 to 100 ppm of the organ in mercury. There's also been a fair amount of industrial medicine experience with mercury which shows that the form of mercury taken up leads to different effects in the human and to different final concentrations in different organs. Hughes published a paper in the *Annals of the New York Academy of Science* (1957) which documented about five different human cases. The five different types of mercury poisoning showed, on autopsy, concentrations on the order of 10 to 100 ppm.

VOICE FROM AUDIENCE: You might mention that mercury poisoning is not a new phenomenon. What about the mad hatter?

MORGAN: Oh yes, Mike Kessick did some research on the mad hatter for me. Mercuric nitrate and nitric acid mixtures were used for a long time in the felting of hides. There was a high incidence of insanity, delusions, blindness, and physiological breakdowns of various types associated with this particular occupation exposure— exposure to high concentrations of mercury. And it was mercury in an organic form I suspect—an interaction of mercuric salts with the organic material in the original furs.

QUESTION: Wasn't the mechanism for getting it into the body actually through the skin in this case, or was it breathing?

MORGAN: I understood that it was by breathing, but I could be mistaken.

QUESTION: Where does mercury pollution come from?

MORGAN: About 20 to 30 percent seems to be associated with chlorine alkali manufacture, which is the largest industrial user of mercury. It is used in agricultural chemicals, to a large extent as organic mercurials. And about 20 percent of the total annual use in the United States is for electrical and electronic equipment. Some of this is being inventoried, some of it is being burned, and some of it is being thrown away in the environment. A lot of it is very hard to account for.

ANSON: What do you see in your view as the biggest crying need: more data, more techniques, more people, more crusades, more control?

MORGAN: One of the greatest needs that I see is more control, now that we know or at least have a feeling for the magnitude of the problem. We have it within our capability to identify every source of mercury in the industrial and domestic areas. I think we should be spending much of our regulatory governmental manpower in that area. The second need I see is for quantitative research on certain unresolved questions in the medical and physiological areas. You're going to have a very hard time when you try to shut off the flow of mercury on the grounds that you *think* there is a very high risk associated with it. After the Alomogordo, New Mexico, case the FDA was able to put a ban on the chemical but the industry went to court and within about three months got the ban lifted. The chemical is, I believe, again on the market. Now there's an argument that says, let the user beware, but I would argue that we have to look much more closely at the need for control by our society of dangerous elements in the environment. I'm not arguing for a great deal more sophisticated chemical analysis. I'm arguing for a lot more physiological work and some biological work on the ecological properties of the system. I think that's more important than more and more *data* obtained throughout the environment.

QUESTION: I would like to know something about the organization that gave you all these data—is that scientific interest or is it government concern?

MORGAN: I think in most of the cases I identified the author associated with the publication—all of this work has been published by individual scientists working in universities, oceanographic institutes, state laboratories, the City of Los Angeles, the County of Los Angeles. Lodge's work was supported by the NSF or USPHS at the National Center for Atmospheric Research. There's a variety of mechanisms for support and of reasons for interest in both the mercury and the lead problem. For example, the work on the distribution of lead particles near highways was done by scientists in the College of Agriculture at Rutgers University because of their interest in the effects of lead on agriculture. I don't think there's any simple support mechanism, or any one single reason behind the variety of data that I've tried to show here.

QUESTION: I get the feeling from what you've said that most of the sources of pollution by mercury could be corrected at no great economic loss—whereas the cure of smog involves a rather difficult change in automobiles that people are unwilling to make. The use of mercurials as fungicides I suspect would be easy to change into something else.

MORGAN: That's my own feeling. I've not personally worked on the mercury or the lead problem. My own research interest has been elsewhere, and so I come upon it almost as an outsider, except that I have a primary interest in the environment. My overall reaction to the mercury and lead problems is that lead would apparently cause more severe economic dislocations at the outset to a large industry with a large investment in the use of tetraethyllead. Mercury control, seemingly, would cause less of a strain. I think in both cases that the change could be made if the effort were made by the legislatures at the federal and state levels. I don't think it's a much more difficult question than that. There are still a lot of questions about the prior accumulation in the biosphere. There's an awful lot of stuff out there already, in some intermediate stage between having been turned loose and being on its way to the ocean or atmosphere. But from now on I think that controls would solve the rest of the future problem.

M. R. BARUSCH

is a career employee of the Chevron Research Company, Richmond, California. He received an A.B. (1940) in chemistry, and an A.M. (1941) and Ph.D. (1944) in organic chemistry, all from Stanford University. Dr. Barusch joined the Research and Development Department of the Standard Oil Company of California in 1943 shortly before this department became a separate subsidiary, which is now named the Chevron Research Company. He is the author of papers and patents on fuel additives and the chemistry of hydrocarbon combustion. His interests during most of his professional career have concentrated on engine fuel additives, and he was manager of the division that did the chemical research that led to the development of gasoline detergents and eventually F–310 (a registered trademark for polybutene amine gasoline additive). Since 1969, he has been the Manager of the Greases and Industrial Oils Division.

CHAIRMAN
William H. Corcoran
*Vice President for Institute Relations
and Professor of Chemical Engineering
Caltech*

M. R. BARUSCH

History of
the Development of F-310

CORCORAN: This is a continuation of our discussion of society and chemistry. Today, we have the opportunity to listen to Dr. Maurice Barusch, who is the head of the Fuel Additives Division for the Standard Oil Company of California, speak to us about F-310. Obviously, at least in Southern California, F-310 has been a controversial subject. It is my understanding that Dr. Barusch in his presentation will be speaking factually on the history of the development of F-310. What questions you would ask of him subsequently I would leave to you, but I told Dr. Barusch that we are analytical and objective, and those are the characteristics of questions that he can expect to be asked. It is my pleasure now to introduce Dr. Barusch.

BARUSCH: Thank you very much. I do plan to emphasize just how this development came about and the role of the technical man in initiating the research and overcoming the problems that had to be solved in order to bring this development to its conclusion. I should correct Professor Corcoran. I am the *former* head of the Fuel Additives Division, having left this position more than a year and a half ago. Some of the most recent work I will be discussing was concluded after I left the fuel field, and I do not have the first-hand, deep knowledge of this recent work that I have of earlier efforts.

You may be interested in knowing how a young chemist became involved in this field. Years ago I faced the same problems with which many of you graduate students are concerned. I received my doctorate in chemistry during World War II and was among the last of the graduate students permitted to finish. There was a little matter of a draft then, the same one that is bothering some of you now. Shortly after I had left the university, the draft forced all draftable graduate students to terminate their studies for either essential industries or the Army. At that time, petroleum research provided two "essential fields." One of these was research on aviation gasoline. Some of my earliest work consisted of efforts to increase the knock-limited power available from aircraft gasoline. This was an anti-knock problem, so at the conclusion of the war I had had some experience in the fuel-additives field. One of my supervisors foresaw that the gasoline business might eventually become much like the soap business had been prior to World War II, a business where strong advertising campaigns were used to sell the product. It was thought that gasoline marketers would face a highly competitive situation, so we should try to develop something significant on which to base claims for improved performance. I was assigned the job of devising fuel additives that would provide the basis for such legitimate claims.

In the brochure announcing these seminars, it was stated that I would speak on how developments such as F-310 come about. "Do they come about through pressures from the marketplace?" It is my experience that in a mature field, such as gasoline quality, worthwhile ideas are generally conceived by the individual researcher. Generally, marketing people do not provide the basis for such ideas.

In searching for an opportunity to develop new product features for gasolines, it was difficult to originate promising ideas. The only way to proceed seemed to be to do basic research that would provide information that competitors did not possess. Hopefully, such new knowledge would lead to new ideas. It was therefore decided to enter the area of combustion research, and a project was initiated that has been active ever since. When combustible mixtures of most hydrocarbons are heated in air, spontaneous ignition generally proceeds through a two-stage process. Following an initial induction period, a slight pressure pulse can be observed. This is followed by a second induction period, and finally explosion occurs. Coinciding with the first pressure pulse, a feeble, blue luminescence sweeps through the mixture. The luminescence can be observed in a dark room if the pupils of the eyes are well dilated. Relatively small amounts of heat are generated, so the phenomenon has been termed a "cool flame."

These flames were discovered prior to the turn of the century. In the middle 1940s, interest in them was rekindled by a Britisher, Professor A. D. Walsh, now at the University of Dundee, Scotland. This process intrigued us, and we decided to concentrate our initial efforts in this area. Our first idea in attacking this problem was to try to stabilize cool flames from a pure hydrocarbon by flowing

Figure 1

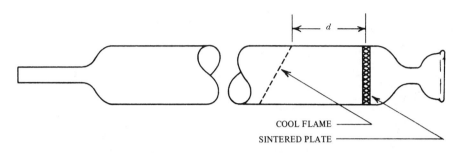

COOL FLAME TUBE

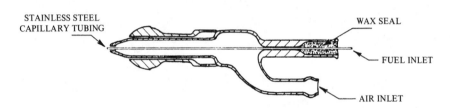

FUEL ASPIRATOR

combustible fuel–air mixtures through a straight glass tube maintained in an air furnace. This proved to be easy to accomplish. Figure 1, which is from a paper more than 20 years old, shows a diagram of the apparatus employed. Heating the tube to a temperature of the order of 300°C, we managed to stabilize the cool flame as a plane shown by the dashed line. The position of the flame could be altered at will by changing flow rates.

We proceeded to study the chemistry and kinetics of the reactions involved and soon observed that tarry materials condensed at the end of the tube where lower temperatures prevailed. If the effluent products from the tube were quenched in a dry-ice bath, a clear liquid condensate was obtained. Evaporation in vacuum below room temperature produced a syrupy, clear liquid that was explosive. When the effluent from the tube was cooled only to about 100°C, a varnish-like material resulted which interested us as a material related to engine deposits.

Since this time, it has been established by others that cool flames are important in the gasoline engine. They generally occur in every combustion cycle of a gasoline engine in the unburned gas

Figure 2

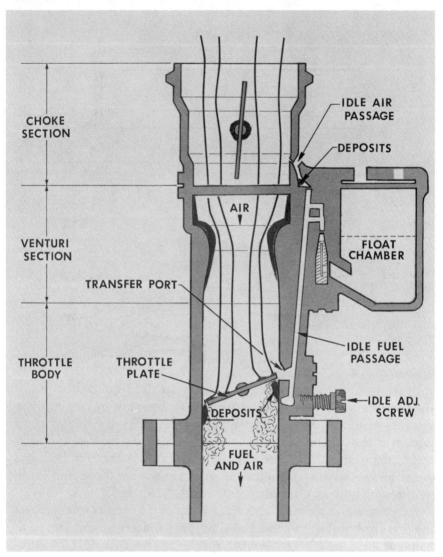

ahead of the flame front. These reactions contribute to many of the problems of the gasoline engine.

Similar combustion work was done in a motored engine, a gasoline engine operated without spark, where the heat of compression initiated the cool flames. Massive amounts of cool-flame combustion products could be conveniently accumulated from the motored engine for study.

While this combustion work was underway, a team of our engineers was studying some of the practical problems of gasoline engines in the field. I should say that I am oversimplifying this story, but this is required for a concise treatment. We periodically survey field problems to assess their importance and determine if our products have deficiencies. Our team of engineers set out to determine what major problems were plaguing our customers. They determined that at that time, the most frequent mechanical problem experienced by repair garages was a problem caused by carburetor deposition. Figure 2, the diagram of a carburetor, illustrates the cause of the deposit problem. Small amounts, milligram quantities, of solids build up adjacent to the throttle plate. Analysis of these deposits showed them to be similar to the products being obtained from cool-flame reactions. It did not take long to discover that a major source of the carburetor deposits was the blowby that was vented from the crankcase. Blowby is gas from the combustion chamber that works its way past the rings into the crankcase. In those days the crankcase was vented directly to the atmosphere. The vent pipe was located beneath the engine. When a stationary car was idling, the hot gases rose up into the air intake. Since air filters are not designed to function at low speed, gummy materials can go right into the carburetor. Here a kind of cyclone is created, and solids or liquids impinging on the walls leave a carburetor deposit. Another source of deposits is the exhaust gases and other airborne contaminants that the engine breathes during ordinary operation.

This was a common problem. If eliminated, we would have the basis for a unique product claim. Now that we thought we understood the mechanism of carburetor-deposit formation, the next step was to duplicate the process in the laboratory. A carburator was modified encasing the throttle plate in a glass collar. To accelerate deposit formation, all the blowby from the engine was introduced with the fuel–air mixture. Running the engine through a cycle simulating operation in traffic, in a matter of a few hours a dark deposit would build up on the glass collar.

Here now was an opportunity for product improvement. One way would be to change the gasoline composition. Indeed, these deposits have now been minimized in this manner in many modern fuels. Another idea to combat the deposit is to introduce a detergent into the gasoline which would wash the deposit away. When the throttle is opened, the whole area around the throttle plate is bathed in gasoline. The presence of a detergent could cleanse the surface. Some of you will recall seeing advertisements claiming this property for gasoline. At our laboratories much experience had been accumulated using oil-soluble detergents in lubricating oils, but no one had previously thought of using such materials in gasolines. We proceeded to test a number of these oil-soluble detergents for deposit removal. Dozens and eventually hundreds of the materials developed in the lube-oil work were evaluated with little success.

We finally decided to try a long-chain hydrocarbon amine as a detergent. In those days, work with lube-oil additives had avoided such materials because of side problems they introduced. We immediately noticed significant cleansing of the deposits.

At this point, we faced the typical problem of the applied organic chemist. We had a test to simulate a well-defined service problem, and we had a compound that would alleviate the problem. Efforts turned to optimizing the molecular structure, and we proceeded to systematically search for a material that was sufficiently effective and practical for this purpose. The structure of the additive found to be the optimum was

$$C_{17}H_{33}C{\overset{\displaystyle O}{\diagdown}}_{NHCH_2CH_2NHCH_2CH_2OH}$$

This is a compound derived from oleic acid and an article of commerce, hydroxyethylethylenediamine. It proved to be an extremely effective material for removing carburetor deposits. A concentration of 30 ppm of this additive proved to clean a very dirty carburetor within a few thousand miles.

Research now had a product that researchers felt should be attractive for marketing, especially since its use was relatively inexpensive. Our business people, however, were quite skeptical as to how well this feature could be sold to the public. Eventually, they became convinced of its value and decided to introduce it into Chevron gasolines. Thus, way back in 1954, the additive was commercialized, with a vigorous campaign somewhat reminiscent of the F-310 campaign, although not as big. It was named the World's First Detergent-Action Gasoline. The additive was used exclusively in our own products for about two years, but we knew that in the long run our competitors could develop their own detergents. Consequently, in 1956, the additive was licensed to the Ethyl Corporation, who sold it nationwide.

For some time this additive was the most widely used of the gasoline detergents. For several years it was present in more than half the country's premium gasolines.

Figure 3 shows a photograph of the throttle-body area of a dou-

Figure 3

**Without Detergent Gasoline
20,000 Miles**

**After Using Detergent Gasoline
4,000 Miles**

ble-barrelled carburetor which contains typical carburetor deposits accumulated over several thousand miles. The lower photograph illustrates the benefit of using 30 ppm of the detergent.

Once the exploratory research is complete, considerable time

Figure 4

elapses before decisions are made to introduce the additive commercially. Additional time is required to build manufacturing plants. Thus, before this gasoline detergent was actually in commercial use, we were looking for ways of expanding our ideas for applications of detergents in gasolines.

Having a jump on our competition, we knew there were other deposits in the intake system that might be affected, and it was obvious that the use of detergents could be extended. Figure 4 shows deposits in the intake system which the Detergent-Action additive was not cleansing. This picture is of a manifold sawed in half. The fuel–air mixture is transported from the carburetor through the manifold to the various cylinders. In this sectioned manifold you see the heavy deposits around the stove area. The stove in the manifold is a heat exchanger where exhaust gases help volatilize the gasoline. The heavy carbonaceous deposits shown here were commonly found in vehicles confined to city driving, particularly to taxicabs and delivery vehicles. In some instances, manifolds were found containing so much deposit that a pencil could hardly be inserted through these deposits. Deposits were also observed in the intake ports of the engine.

In the case of the intake valve, the deposits differ chemically from the manifold deposits. The valve deposits are extremely hard and brittle. They are rich in lead compounds and extremely resistant to detergents. The lead content results from the phenomenon of value overlap; the intake valve opens just before the exhaust stroke of the piston is completed and a small amount of exhaust gas puffs back into the intake manifold. Lead compounds thus can condense on the intake value and contribute to these very heavy deposits.

We were using a very small amount of detergent in our gasolines. One obvious thing considered was to increase the concentration. Eventually, it was found that a concentration of about 280 ppm, almost 10-fold greater than the Detergent-Action concentration, could clean up the intake manifold and the intake parts. But a side effect made it impractical to use such high concentrations of our additive. When the detergent was present at these high concentrations, a water-emulsion problem developed. There is a small but real solubility of water in hydrocarbons, and gasolines in commerce frequently were saturated with water. Warm fuels leave the refinery frequently via a pipeline. As the temperature of the gasoline drops, a water phase separates. The pipeline must operate under highly turbulent conditions. In the presence of a high concentration of the Detergent-Action additive, emulsions would be produced that would prevent the water from settling from the gasolines at a practical rate after the fuel emerged from the pipeline.

We did not know at that time that it was possible to find an effective detergent that would not cause this emulsion problem. However, considerable work resulted in a modified molecule in which the hydroxyl group was eliminated. This new compound was effective in removing both the manifold and port deposits, if used at sufficient high concentrations.

Figure 5 illustrates the advantages of a clean intake system. These curves plot horsepower versus speed. The lower curve was obtained in the engine that had heavy synthetic intake valve and port deposits applied to simulate the deposits that are encountered in a high-mileage engine used in predominately stop-and-go driving. By removal of the port deposits, the middle curve resulted. Fur-

Figure 5

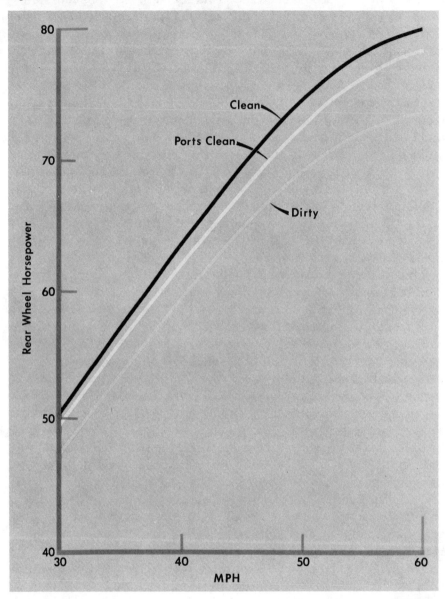

ther removal of the value deposits increased power output to the top curve. Synthetic deposits were used in this work because naturally formed deposits have a tendency to break off during full throttle-power measurements and produce erroneous results. At this point our technology permitted the removal of intake-port and manifold deposits. However, to achieve this required about tenfold as much additive as we had been using. Researchers again tried to sell our business people on the new additive. Marketing personnel were reluctant to accept it, pointing out that, although such consumers were experiencing considerable deposits on valves, the average passenger vehicle was not troubled by manifold deposits. Considerable debate ensued to justify the increased cost of the additive in the marketplace. It eventually was decided to use the additive for selected wholesale accounts—fleet accounts, where many vehicles are managed by one organization. Since elaborate records are often kept on fleets of vehicles, the influence of fuel-quality changes on maintenance costs can easily be determined. The high concentration of 280 ppm of the additive we termed our Extended Detergent. It was introduced into gasoline delivered to many fleets starting in 1959.

Some years after introduction of the Extended Detergent, limited problems were encountered, particularly one using certain new types of oil formulations in a newly designed engine. Research showed the cause of this problem to be an additive-lube-oil-formulation incompatibility which resulted when a small fraction of additive worked its way by the rings. Some fuel plus additive was oxidized in the process to decrease its solubility and become incompatible with the new oil formulation so that deposits formed in the ring-belt area. In one engine, sufficient ring fouling was experienced that the use of the additive was curtailed in that make of car, although in other service the extended detergent was successfully used until our modern materials were developed.

We continued our efforts to solve the difficult problem of valve deposits. Figure 6 shows typical heavy deposits on passenger-car intake valves. In the valve on the left, it can be seen that the deposit has been fractured and a portion lost. These deposits are brittle. Although it occurs rarely, large bits of the deposits can also fall down in the combustion chamber and cause damage. I emphasize that this is a rare problem, but it is a problem that concerns automobile manufacturers.

This was sufficient justification for continuing efforts to develop detergents to remove valve deposits, with their high lead content. For years we were unsuccessful in simulating the formation and removal of these deposits in the laboratory. Much of our exploratory work actually was conducted in vehicles operated on the road. Taxicabs were used for this purpose, as they accumulated mileage relatively rapidly. Still, months were required to produce the heavy deposits. Years went by in our efforts to find more effective detergents. The finding that in one specific service, our extended deter-

Figure 6

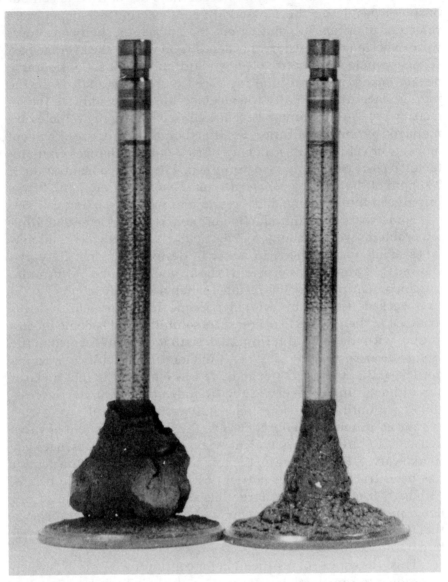

gent had had trouble eventually caused us to evaluate higher-molecular-weight molecules. We had been avoiding such materials because at low concentration they were not among the most effective materials in the glass-throttle-body test. Eventually, we came on a class of compounds, the polybutene amines, that solved this valve problem. F-310 is one of this class.

Having found that certain members of the polybutene amine

family were highly effective, we went through the usual structure-optimization efforts. Eventually, a material was devised that at 250 ppm essentially cleaned up the entire intake system. Further, this material proved to help prevent deposits in the crankcase zone, as you will see later. However, this additive again was a bad emulsifier. Since the emulsion problem is not critical in the fleets, this material was actually used in fleet accounts for awhile.

We were eventually successful in changing the molecular structure enough to produce a product with adequate water-settling properties. Moreover, a third agent was found, a demulsifier, that improved the emulsion properties further. Results with the changed product showed that 400 ppm, a very large amount of gasoline additive, was prefered for the desired performance. By comparison, at the time our F-310 advertising campaign was initiated, most carburetor detergents were used at concentrations at or below 30 ppm. I believe there was a gasoline additive on the market whose recommended use concentration was 85 ppm. This material was probably not all active ingredient and proved not very effective in our tests. Our concentration of 400 ppm refers to active ingredients.

The following illustration shows the performance of the new additive and demonstrates that we could clean up dirty intake valves. Figure 7 shows the results of driving a taxicab for more than 20,000 miles on the new additive.

Incidentally, soon after using the gasoline detergent, the deposit starts to become soft rather than brittle, eliminating the danger of deposit fracture.

In the days since the original development of the Detergent-Action additive, all new cars sold were equipped with positive crankcase-ventilation devices. These devices conducted the fumes from the crankcase back into the intake system and into the combustion chamber. None of the blowby products are expelled in the atmosphere. This causes the severity of the intake-system deposit problem to be much greater. Indeed, we found that our original detergent had no longer been able to keep the throttle body completely clean. The new polybutene amine, on a weight basis, was not as effective a carburetor detergent as the original material; but using it at nearly 15 times the early concentration, it is totally effective.

Tests were performed using taxis of the Oakland Yellow Cab Company. Valve deposits, which had built up in the throttle body of the carburetor of a taxi run on conventional detergent gasoline, were markedly reduced after the engine had been exposed to 400

Figure 7

ppm of the new additive for a few thousand miles. The same was true of intake-port deposits.

One of the pleasant surprises we had with polybutene amines is the finding that enough of them work their way by the rings to be highly effective detergents in the crankcase zone. Here our additives do not generally clean up the engine parts, but they prevent deposits from forming. This is important because the deposits around the piston-ring zone contribute to high oil consumption. Comparisons of side cover plates from a taxi run on conventional gasoline to one from an engine run a similar distance on the same gasoline containing the F-310 type of additive show that the sludging is prevented. Similar striking results were noted for other parts of the engine.

At this point, the research team believed that a near millennium had been achieved. Most of the offensive deposits in the gasoline engine could be controlled. The experts honestly thought, and still do think, that cars operated on this high concentration of additive probably would go severalfold more miles between overhauls. Engine overhauls are normally necessitated because of either deposits in the engine or because of wear. Controlling deposit formation eliminates a major contributor to maintenance problems.

The business people whom we contacted were impressed with the technological achievement but were equally impressed with the high cost associated with the use of 400 ppm of the new additive. They repeatedly pointed out that a manufacturer cannot produce a product more expensive than the competition and stay in business. The benefits of a new additive would not be apparent until after

Figure 8

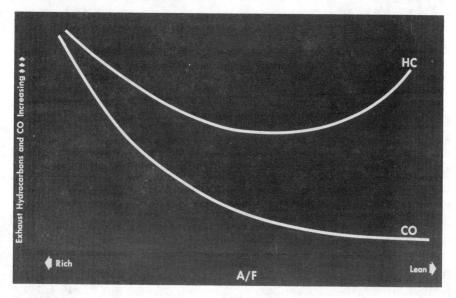

years of use, but most original car owners keep their cars only 2 to 3 years. The used-car purchaser does not know the history of the gasoline purchased by the original owner.

But increased gasoline mileage, on the other hand, makes a gasoline more salable. Also, it was believed that decreased emissions to the atmosphere would be an attractive future.

Intuitively, a car with heavy deposits should experience decreased mileage. Older cars tend to consume more gasoline, prob-

Figure 9

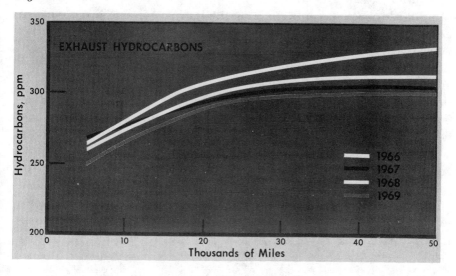

ably at least in part because of engine deposits. Data were also available showing that deposits contribute to emissions because they cause automobiles to operate with fuel–air mixtures richer than optimum. It was decided to make measurements on these effects in actual road service.

To this point, we have described areas in the engine where the additive is highly effective in controlling deposits. On the other hand, the combustion chamber accumulates deposits, and no claims are made that the new additive affects these either constructively or adversely. The important areas affecting emissions are the entire carburetor area and the positive crankcase ventilation (PCV) valve. If the PCV valve sticks closed, as it will when it gets dirty, the fuel–air mixture becomes excessively rich. The new additive cleans up the PCV valves and essentially removes all deposits from the carburetor.

Figure 8 illustrates well-known data showing how emissions from an engine change with fuel–air mixture. As the mixture is leaned, less carbon monoxide is produced by an engine. However, the gasoline engine operates at maximum efficiency when it is slightly richer than stoichiometric. As the mixture is leaned, misfiring can result; and hydrocarbons emitted increase rapidly.

The Air Resources Board published data, which are plotted in Figure 9, show how the emissions of hydrocarbons increase with mileage. The first few thousand miles are omitted from the curves to avoid the situation when combustion-chamber deposits were building up rapidly. These combustion-chamber deposits soon come to equilibrium. It is our opinion that the major efforts shown here are due to carburetor and PCV valve deposits.

Board measurements showing the increase in carbon monoxide emissions with mileage provide concrete reasons for believing that deposit control would result in reduced emissions to the atmosphere. It was decided to contract for accelerated tests to measure emission buildup in vehicles and to evaluate the effectiveness of the new additive. Scott Research Laboratories, an organization in Southern California that does contract air-pollution work for the federal government and for industry, was commissioned to do the test. The Scott organization purchased a fleet of eight vehicles in reasonably good shape which had each accumulated 6000 to 30,000 miles. Before being placed on test the carburetor of each vehicle was cleaned, the car tuned, and a new PCV valve inserted. No other work was done on the engines. All other deposits were left intact. Scott Laboratories was supplied with a gasoline representative of the

Figure 10

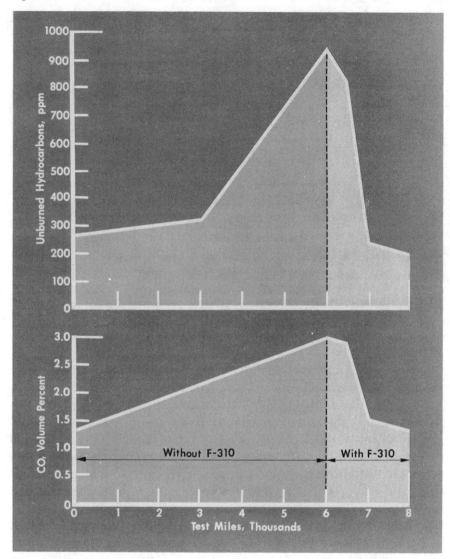

poorest 5 to 10 percent of the gasoline on the market in deposit-forming tendencies. This gasoline was selected in a deliberate effort to provide an accelerated severe test. Using this gasoline, operating the cars on the road in a cycle representing city driving, deposits built up rapidly. Figure 10 presents typical results from one of the 13 tests conducted. Within 6000 miles of operation on this high-deposit-forming gasoline, hydrocarbon emissions increased to a very high level. After the 6000 miles of operations, the car was emitting heavy black smoke of the type that some of you have seen

Figure 11

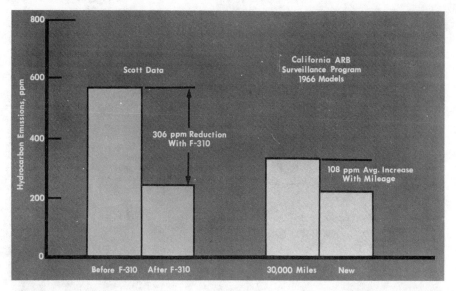

in the black-balloon advertisements. It was not alleged that these high emissions were typical, but that they were examples of what can happen when carburetor and PCV valve deposits get sufficiently severe.

The same car was then run on our gasoline containing the new additive. Within 2000 miles the hydrocarbon content had dropped, to, or actually slightly below, the initial emission level. Carbon monoxide emissions behaved in a similar fashion.

In all cases, the 13 tests gave similar results. Mileages of up to about 20,000 miles were required to produce the excessive emissions. On switching to the new gasoline, all cars were cleansed rapidly; and in most cases were restored to their original emission levels within 2000 miles of operation. From the data obtained in the Scott tests (Figure 11) it can be noted that, on the average, more than 50 percent reduction in hydrocarbon emissions was obtained by use of the additive.

This was admittedly an accelerated test. Surveillance from the Air Resources Board show that the possible effect in the average car would be much less. However, it had been proved that the dirtiest vehicle would respond in spectacular fashion to the new gasoline.

The Scott Carpenter ads were based on these test data. When those ads appeared, the public reacted. Some people were highly impressed, some were skeptical, and some were incensed.

Without our knowledge, Los Angeles County decided to test the

Figure 12

MILEAGE AT START OF TEST	TEST MILES	HYDRO-CARBON EMISSIONS AT START, (ppm)	HYDRO-CARBON EMISSIONS AT END, (ppm)	CARBON MONOXIDE EMISSIONS, % AT START	CARBON MONOXIDE EMISSIONS, % AT END
56,327	1,433	409	294	2.89	1.87
59,958	2,093	501	351	3.24	1.88
46,160	1,102	514	456	2.83	2.12
34,290	678	344	266	3.28	2.10
37,394	1,927	420	274	2.07	.77
30,006	1,762	374	299	3.06	1.29
44,022*	1,499*	427*	323*	2.90*	1.67*

*Average

gasoline for themselves. Los Angeles County vehicles at that time were buying a competitive gasoline that had been selected in the usual way—the lowest bidder received the contract. On their own initiative, without our knowledge, six of their vehicles were put on our commercial Chevron gasoline (containing F-310). The results are tabulated in Figure 12.

Data accumulated in the shefiff's cars are surprisingly consistent. One of the cars was driven on the gasoline less than 700 miles. In every case, hydrocarbons emitted decreased, and carbon monoxide emissions went down.

Our company was ignorant of the progress of the sheriff's tests, and while they were proceeding, we decided to obtain more extensive road data. Being the lowest bidder, we received the contract to supply the automobile fleet owned and operated by Orange County —more than 1000 vehicles (Ford and Plymouths exclusively). The maintenance practices of this fleet are extremely good. Engines are tuned every 10,000 miles. This caused us to be concerned that the cars were maintained in such good condition that the effect from F-310 might be minimized. It should be emphasized that we had just

Figure 13

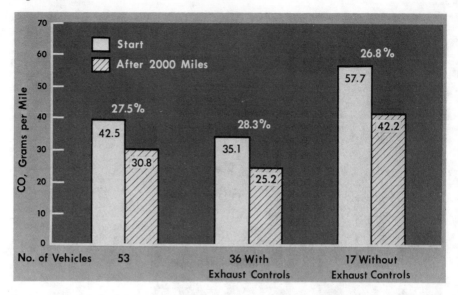

been awarded this contract, and that a competitor had previously supplied this fleet.

The management of the fleet picked out a sample of about 50 cars selected to be representative in models and age of the entire fleet. Again, the Scott Laboratories were awarded a contract to obtain measurements on emissions from every car before and after running on the new gasoline. An average of about 12 percent reduction in hydrocarbons was measured after the fleet had run about 2000 miles on the new gasoline. Data were segregated for the vehicles fitted with exhaust controls and those without. Starting in 1966, all new cars sold in California were equipped with exhaust controls to lower the emissions. These cars showed a somewhat smaller effect from F-310. In this test an even larger effect from the additive was obtained in controlling carbon monoxide (Figure 13).

One of the operators measuring emissions noticed an effect on the filters used to protect the analyzing equipment. None of the cars at the start of the test were producing visible smoke. However, black deposits did form on the filters of some of the cars while the emissions were being measured at the test start. No such deposits were present on the filters after the cars had run on F-310.

This was highly reassuring; however, we realized that no extensive test data were available representative of all the cars on the road. Efforts were made to get the Air Resources Board to conduct a test, completely independently, to measure the effectiveness of the new gasoline. They really were not staffed to do this. Further, they

Figure 14

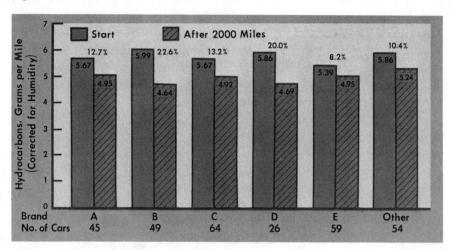

feared that if they conducted such a test they might have to do similar evaluations for other gasoline manufacturers. As a result, they conducted only a limited test with inconclusive findings. We were unable to get a public agency to do an adequate test of this sort although we still have not given up hope.

It was decided to initiate a test on a large number of vehicles selected to be typical of the car population of the State of California. This was now practical because our gasoline was widely available. The site chosen was right here in the Pasadena neighborhood in the parking lot of the Rose Bowl. It is isolated, and we hoped our activities there would not awaken the interest of the press. A marketing-research organization was contracted to select a fleet of about 500 cars that would be representative of the California car population. Our statisticians requested a test on about 300 cars, and it was assumed that an initial population of 500 cars might yield 300 vehicles that would complete the test. This marketing-research organization contacted people living within a 5-mile radius of the Rose Bowl.

From California state motor vehicle registration data they selected a sample of car owners who signified willingness to come to the Rose Bowl site and have their vehicles tested. These people were told they were going to test gasolines in their cars. They were not told what company was supporting the test or whose gasoline they would be testing. They were promised a credit card good for gasoline and makeup oil for about a 2000-mile test. This credit card was not usable for any maintenance work. About 455 cars were thus brought to the Rose Bowl parking lot. The fleet was representative of the State's population of cars. While emissions were measured from the automobiles, the owners were interviewed to determine their maintenance practices. They were given no advice as to how to maintain their cars. They did not know which gasoline other people in the test would be purchasing. To induce them to complete the test, each car owner was promised 10 books of Blue Chip stamps if they returned at the end of 2000 miles. The people turned out to be most cooperative. In arranging this sample of drivers, all car owners who indicated they had been purchasers of Chevron gasoline prior to the test were excluded.

Most of the 455 cars did return for their final measurements. Prior to analyzing the data, all cars that had undergone maintenance work or deteriorated mechanically were eliminated from the survey. Apparently, the older cars required more maintenance work. One car returned at the conclusion of the test with a new engine in it and was, naturally, eliminated.

The emission measurements were made by contract with the Olson Laboratories. Almost 300 vehicles provided usable data, that is, accumulated sufficient mileage during the test and did not have their engines tuned or overhauled. The average car experienced a reduction in hydrocarbons emitted of about 14 percent. The results were corrected for changes in humidity during the test period. (Had we not corrected for the humidity, the effect of hydrocarbon emissions would have been somewhat less, around 11 percent.) In this test, little difference is seen between the effect produced with the older and the new cars. We obtained a similar reduction for carbon monoxide emissions. In Figure 14 the data are analyzed based on the source of gasoline which the car owner indicated that he had purchased prior to the test. Cars that were run previously on the five major brands or on the minor brands lumped together all showed a similar average reduction in hydrocarbons emitted after driving about 2000 miles on the gasoline containing F-310.

We think this is a definitive test. All major competitive gasolines have been compared with our new product. We still hope that in the future, a federal agency will independently make a comparable study.

I hope that this talk has given you some insight into how a research scientist in industry approaches his job: in particular, how we at Chevron Research developed the fuel additives used today in Standard Oil gasoline. The complete story of the product development is complex, but this was the part we, as scientists, played.

MAX DELBRÜCK

is a professor of biology at Caltech. He began his scientific career in physics, getting his Ph.D. under Max Born and W. Heitler in Göttingen in 1930. He was interested in quantum theory and in nuclear physics. Stimulated by working with Niels Bohr in Copenhagen in 1932, he began to consider the application of principles of physics to biological problems. He came to the United States in 1937 and began his pioneering studies on bacterial viruses, for which he received the Nobel prize in physiology and medicine in 1969.

CHAIRMAN
Norman R. Davidson
Professor and Executive Officer
for Chemistry
Caltech

MAX DELBRÜCK

Homo Scientificus
According to Beckett

DAVIDSON: The original title suggested to our speaker by our valiant organizer was "Basic Research Responsibilities." The title submitted by the speaker to the organizer was *"Homo Scientificus* According to Beckett." As far as I know, there are two Becketts in history. One of them was killed in a cathedral and the other won a Nobel prize for writing plays. That's all I know about the seminar and I'm looking forward to hearing it.

DELBRÜCK: In December 1970 Bill Beranek wrote me a letter saying that he wanted one of these sessions devoted to the subject: "The Responsibility of the Scientist to Society with Respect to Pure Basic Research." He added a number of questions, which I will quickly answer, as best I can.

Question 1: Is pure science to be regarded as overall beneficial to society?

Answer: It depends much on what you consider benefits. If you look at health, long life, transportation, communication, education, you might be tempted to say yes. If you look at the enormous social-economic dislocations, at the prospect of an immense famine in India, brought on by the advances of public health science and nutrition science, at strains on our psyches due to the imbalance between technical developments and our limited ability to adjust to the pace of change, you might be tempted to say no. Clearly, the present state of the world—to which science has contributed much —leaves a great deal to be desired, and much to be feared. So I write down:

(1) SCIENCE BENEFICIAL?
    DOUBTFUL.

133

Question 2: Is pure science to be considered as something potentially harmful?

Answer: Most certainly! Every child knows that it is potentially exceedingly harmful. Our lecture series here on environmental problems concerns just a small aspect. The menace of blowing ourselves up by atom bombs, doing ourselves in by chemical or biological warfare, or by population explosion, is certainly with us. I consider the environment thing a trivial question, by comparison—like housekeeping. In any home, the dishes have to be washed, the floors swept, the beds made, and there must be rules as to who is allowed to produce how much stink and noise, and where in the house. When the garbage piles up, these questions become pressing. But they are momentary problems. Once the house is in order, you still want to *live* in it, not just sit around enjoying its orderliness. I would be sorry to see Caltech move heavily into this type of applied research. Again I write:

(2) SCIENCE POTENTIALLY HARMFUL?
     DEFINITELY.

Question 3: Should a scientist consider possible ramifications of his research and their effects on society, or is this something not only difficult to do but perhaps better done by others?

Answer: I think it is impossible for anybody, scientist or not, to foresee the ramifications. We might say that that is a *definition* of basic science. *Vide* Einstein's discovery in 1905 of the equivalence of mass and energy and the development of atomic weaponry.

(3) CONSIDER RAMIFICATIONS?
     IMPOSSIBLE.

So much for Bill's original questions in December.

I agreed to come to the lectures and then decide whether I thought I had something to contribute. After having listened to a series of lectures on environmental problems, such as lead poisoning, mercury poisoning, on smog, on waste disposal, on fuel additives, and to Dan Kevles' and George Hammond's more general talks, I told Bill that I had found the series interesting and worthwhile but that I felt most uneasy about where I might fit in. So he wrote me another letter. Tenacious guy. With more questions. These again I can answer in short order.

Question 4: Why did you choose science as your life's work?

Answer: I think the most relevant answer that I can give to this question is this: I found out at an early age that science is a haven for the timid, the freaks, the misfits. That is more true perhaps for the past than now. If you were a student in Göttingen in the 1920s and went to the seminar "Structure of Matter" which was under the joint auspices of David Hilbert and Max Born, you could well imagine that you were in a madhouse as you walked in. Every one of the persons there was obviously some kind of a severe case. The least you could do was put on some kind of a stutter. Robert Oppenheimer as a graduate student found it expedient to develop a very elegant kind of stutter, the "njum-njum-njum" technique. Thus, if you were an oddball you felt at home.

(4) WHY SCIENTIFIC CAREER?
A HAVEN FOR FREAKS.

Question 5: What is the history of your research?

Answer: Perhaps the most significant aspect is that it throve under adversity. It throve *best* under adversity. I have two periods in mind. The first was in Germany in the middle 1930s under the Nazis when things became quite unpleasant and official seminars became dull. Many people emigrated; others did not leave but were not permitted to go to official seminars. We had a little private club which I organized and which met about once a week, mostly at my mother's house. First just theoretical physicists (I was at that time a theoretical physicist), and then theoretical physicists and biologists. The discussions we had at that time have had a remarkable long-range effect, an effect that astonished us all. This was one adverse situation. Like the great Plague in Florence in 1348, which is the background setting for Bocaccio's *Decameron.* The second one was in this country in the 1940s during the war. I came over in 1937 and was in this country during the war as an enemy alien. And as an enemy alien I secured a job as an instructor of physics at Vanderbilt University in Nashville, Tennessee. You might think that this was a very unpropitious place to be, but it worked out fine. I spent 7½ years there. This situation gave me, in association with Luria (another enemy alien) and in close contact with Hershey (another misfit in society), sufficient leisure to do the first phase of phage research, which has become a cornerstone of molecular genetics. I would not want to generalize to the extent that adversity is the only road to effective innovative science, or art, but the progress of science is often spectacularly disorderly. James Joyce once commented that he survived by "cunning and exile" (and, you might add, by a genius for borrowing money from a number of ladies). I got along all right with the head of the Physics Department at Vanderbilt. He wanted me to do as much physics teaching as possible and as little biology research as possible. I had the opposite desires. We understood each other's attitudes and accommodated each other to a reasonable extent. So, things worked out quite well. At the end of the war I was the oldest instructor on the campus.

(5) HISTORY OF YOUR RESEARCH?
    THROVE UNDER ADVERSITY.

Question 6: Why do you think society should pay for basic research?

Answer: Did I say that society *should* pay for basic research? I didn't. Society does so to a varying extent, and it always astonishes me that it does. It has been part of the current dogma that basic research is good for society, but I would be the last to be dogmatic about the number of dollars society should put up for this goodness. Since I answered the first question with "doubtful," I cannot very well be emphatic in answer to this one.

(6) SOCIETY PAY FOR RESEARCH?
    HOW MUCH?

Question 7: How much control do you feel society should have on deciding which questions you should ask in your research?

Answer: Society can, and does, and must control research enormously, negatively and positively, by selectively cutting off or supplying funds. At present it cuts—not so selectively. That is all right with me, as far as my own research is concerned. I certainly do not think society *owes* me a living or support for my research. If it does not support my research, I can always do something else and not be worse off, perhaps better. However, the question, from society's point of view, is exceedingly complicated. I have no strong views on the matter.

(7) CONTROL OF RESEARCH BY SOCIETY?
A COMPLICATED MATTER, LARGELY OF PROCEDURE.

Question 8: Is there an unwritten scientific oath analogous to the Hippocratic oath which would ask all scientists to use their special expertise and way of thinking to guard against bad effects of science on society, especially today when science is acknowledged to play such a large part in the lives of individuals?

Answer: The original Hippocratic oath, of course, says that you should keep the patient alive under all circumstances. Also that you shouldn't be bribed, shouldn't give poisons, should honor your teachers, and things like that, but essentially to keep the patient alive. And that's a reasonably well defined goal since keeping the patient alive is biologically unambiguous. But to use science for the good of society is not so well defined, therefore I think such an oath could never be written. The only unwritten oath is, of course, that you should be reasonably honest. That is, in fact, carried out to the extent that, although many things you read in the journals are wrong, it is assumed that the author at least believed that he was right. So much so that if somebody deliberately sets out to cheat he can get away with it for years. The number of celebrated cases of cheating or hoaxes would make a long story. But our whole scientific discourse is based on the premise that everybody is *trying* at least to tell the truth, within the limits of his personality; that can be some limit.

(8) HIPPOCRATIC OATH FOR SCIENTISTS?
IMPOSSIBLE TO BE UNAMBIGUOUS.

Question 9: Is science something we do mainly for its own sake, like art or music, or is it something we use as a tool for bettering our physical existence?

Answer: This is a question that turns me on. I think that it bristles with popular misconceptions about the nature of *Homo scientificus,* and therefore maybe I have something to say. Let me start by reading a few passages from an unpublished paper on this species, written in 1942 by a rather preceptive friend, a nonscientist:

The species *Homo scientificus* constitutes a branch of the family *Homo modernibus,* a species easy and interesting to observe but difficult and perplexing to understand.

There are a number of varieties and subvarieties, ranging from the lowliest to the highest. We begin with the humble *professorius scientificus,* whose inclusion in this species is questionable, pass on up through the *geologia* and the large groups of the *chemisto* and *biologia,* with their many hybirds, to the higher orders of the *physicistus* and *mathematicus,* and finally to the lordly *theoretica physicistus,* rarely seen in captivity.

Habitat: These animals range the North American and European continents, and are seldom seen in South America, Africa, or Asia, although a few isolated cases are known in Australia and Russia. [This was written in 1942.] Individuals of the lower orders thrive in most sections of Europe and America but those of the higher orders are to be found only in a few localities, where they live together in colonies. These colonies provide a valuable research field; here one can wander about noting the size, structure, and actions of these peculiar creatures. There is little to fear, for although they may approach one with great curiosity, and attempt to lead one to their lairs, they are not known to be dangerous.

Description: Recent studies of this as-yet-little-understood species have ascertained a number of characteristics by which they may be distinguished. The brain is large and often somewhat soft in spots. In some cases the head is covered with masses of thick, unkempt wool, in others it is utterly devoid of hair and shines like a doorknob. Sometimes there is hair on the face but it never covers the nose. The body covering, when there is any, is without particular color or form, the general appearance is definitely shaggy. The male *scientificus* does not, like the cock or the lion or the bull, delight in flaunting elegantly before the female to catch her eye. Evidently the female is attracted by some other method. We are at a loss as to what this could be, although we have often observed the male scurrying after the female with a wuffley expression on his face. Sometimes he brings her a little gift, such as a bundle of bristles or a bright piece of cellophane, which she accepts tenderly and the trick is done. Occasionally an old king appears from the colony, surrounded by workers. He has soft grey hair on his face, and a pot belly. *Scientificus* is a voracious eater; this is not strange,

for he consumes a great deal of energy each day in playing. In fact, he is one of the best playing animals known.

The *scientificus* undoubtedly have a language of their
own. They take pleasure in jabbering to each other and
often one will stand several hours before a group, holding
forth in monologues; the listeners are for the most part
quiet, and some may even be asleep. However meaningful
this language may be to them, it is utterly incomprehensi-
ble to us. Perhaps the thing which endears this mysterious
creature to us most is his disposition; although there exists
a kind of slavery (the *laboratorio assistantia* being captured to do the dirty work), the *scientificus* does not prey
on other animals of his species and he is neither cruel, sly,
nor domineering. [The author had only studied the species
for one year at that time.] He is an easygoing animal; he
will not, for example, work hard to construct a good dwell-
ing, but is content to live in a damp basement so long as
he can spend most of the day sitting in the sun and rum-
maging among his strange posessions.

The paper then goes on into more detail about the *biologia*. We
will let this suffice by way of a general description of *Homo scientificus*. The description is nice as far as it goes, but too superficial.

Now I want to switch gears and read another piece which I
think goes to the heart of the matter. This is taken from the novel
Molloy by Samuel Beckett. Beckett not only wrote plays—"Happy
Days," "Krapp's Last Tape," "End Game," and "Waiting for Godot"
—but also a number of novels that are less well known. This one,
Molloy, published in the 1950s, concerns an exceedingly lonely and
decrepit old man, and the whole book is a kind of a soliloquy that
he writes down about his life. I have picked one episode that I hope
will illustrate the point I want to make (without having to rub it in
too much). There will be several illustrations to go with this reading
so as to make the argument perfectly clear. At the time of this episode Molloy is a beachcomber at some lonely place.

I took advantage of being at the seaside to lay in a store of
sucking-stones. They were pebbles but I call them stones.
Yes, on this occasion I laid in a considerable store. I dis-
tributed them equally among my four pockets, and sucked
them turn and turn about. This raised a problem which I
first solved in the following way. I had say sixteen stones,

four in each of my four pockets these being the two pockets
of my trousers and the two pockets of my greatcoat. Taking
a stone from the right pocket of my greatcoat, and putting
it in my mouth, I replaced it in the right pocket of my
greatcoat by a stone from the right pocket of my trousers,
which I replaced by a stone from the left pocket of my
trousers, which I replaced by a stone from the left pocket
of my greatcoat, which I replaced by the stone which was
in my mouth, as soon as I had finished sucking it. Thus
there were still four stones in each of my four pockets, but
not quite the same stones. And when the desire to suck took
hold of me again, I drew again on the right pocket of my
greatcoat, certain of not taking the same stone as the last

time. And while I sucked it I rearranged the other stones in the way I have just described. And so on. But this solution did not satisfy me fully. For it did not escape me that, by an extraordinary hazard, the four stones circulating thus might always be the same four. In which case, far from sucking the sixteen stones turn and turn about, I was really only sucking four, always the same, turn and turn about. But I shuffled them well in my pockets, before I began to suck, and again, while I sucked, before transferring them, in the hope of obtaining a more general circulation of the stones from pocket to pocket. But this was only a makeshift that could not long content a man like me. So I began to look for something else. And the first thing I hit upon was that I might do better to transfer the stones four by four, instead of one by one, that is to say, during the sucking, to take the three stones remaining in the right pocket of my greatcoat and replace them by the four in the right pocket of my trousers, and these by the four in the left pocket of my trousers, and these by the four in the left pocket of my greatcoat, and finally these by the three from the right pocket of my greatcoat, plus the one, as soon as I had finished sucking it, which was in my mouth. Yes, it seemed to me at first that by so doing I would arrive at a better result. But on further reflection I had to change my mind and confess that the circulation of the stones four by four came to exactly the same thing as their circulation one by one. For if I was certain of finding each time, in the right pocket of my greatcoat, four stones totally different from their immediate predecessors, the possibility nevertheless remained of my always chancing on the same stone, within each group of four, and consequently of my sucking, not the sixteen turn and turn about as I wished, but in fact four only, always the same, turn and turn about. So I had to seek elsewhere than in the mode of circulation. For no matter how I caused the stones to circulate, I always ran the same risk. It was obvious that by increasing the number of my pockets I was bound to increase my chances of enjoying my stones in the way I planned, that is to say one after the other until their number was exhausted . . . I should have needed sixteen pockets in order to be quite easy in my mind. And for a long time I could see no other conclusion than this, that short of having sixteen

pockets, each with its stone, I could never reach the goal
I had set myself, short of an extraordinary hazard. And if
at a pinch I could double the number of my pockets, were
it only by dividing each pocket in two, with the help of a
few safety-pins, let us say, to quadruple them seemed to be
more than I could manage. And I did not feel inclined to
take all that trouble for a half-measure. For I was beginning to lose all sense of measure, after all this wrestling

and wrangling, and to say, All or nothing. And if I was tempted for an instant to establish a more equitable proportion between my stones and my pockets, by reducing the former to the number of the latter, it was only for an instant. For it would have been an admission of defeat. And sitting on the shore, before the sea, the sixteen stones spread out before my eyes, I gazed at them in anger and perplexity . . . And while I gazed thus at my stones, revolving interminable martingales all equally defective, and crushing handfuls of sand, so that the sand ran through my fingers and fell back on the strand, yes, while thus I lulled my mind and part of my body, one day suddenly it dawned on the former, dimly, that I might perhaps achieve my purpose without increasing the number of my pockets, or reducing the number of my stones, but simply by sacrificing the *principle of trim.* The meaning of this illumination, which suddenly began to sing within me, like a verse of Isaiah, or of Jeremiah, I did not penetrate at once, and notably the word trim, which I had never met with, in this sense, long remained obscure. Finally I seemed to grasp that this word trim could not here mean anything else, anything better, than the distribution of the sixteen stones in four groups of four, one group in each pocket, and that it was my refusal to consider any distribution other than this that had vitiated my calculations until then and rendered the problem literally insoluble. And it was on the basis of this interpretation, whether right or wrong, that I finally reached a solution, inelegant assuredly, but sound, sound. Now I am willing to believe, indeed I firmly believe, that other solutions to this problem might have been found, and indeed may still be found, no less sound, but much more elegant than the one I shall now describe, if I can. And I believe too that had I been a little more insistent, a little more resistant, I could have found them myself. But I was tired, but I was tired, and I contented myself ingloriously with the first solution that was a solution, to this problem. But not to go over the heartbreaking stages through which I passed before I came to it, here it is, in all its hideousness. All (all!) that was necessary was to put for example, to begin with, six stones in the right pocket of my greatcoat, or supply-pocket, five in the right pocket of my trousers, and five in

the left pocket of my trousers, that makes the lot, twice five ten plus six sixteen, and none, for none remained, in the left pocket of my greatcoat, which for the time being remained empty, empty of stones that is, for its usual contents remained, as well as occasional objects. For where do you think I hid my vegetable knife, my silver, my horn, and the other things that I have not yet named, perhaps shall never name. Good. Now I can begin to suck. Watch me closely. I take a stone from the right pocket of my greatcoat, suck it, stop sucking it, put it in the left pocket of my greatcoat, the one empty (of stones). I take a second stone from the right pocket of my greatcoat, suck it, put it in the left pocket of my greatcoat. And so on until the right pocket of my greatcoat is empty (apart from its usual and casual contents) and the six stones I have just sucked, one after the other, are all in the left pocket of my greatcoat. Pausing then, and concentrating, so as not to make a balls of it, I transfer to the right pocket of my greatcoat, in which there are no stones left, the five stones in the right pocket of my trousers, which I replace by the five stones in the left pocket of my greatcoat. At this stage then the left pocket of my greatcoat is again empty of stones, while the right pocket of my greatcoat is again supplied, and in the right way, that is to say with other stones than those I have just sucked . . . Do I have to go on? No, for it is clear that after the next three series, of sucks and transfers, I shall be back where I started, that is to say with the first six stones back in the supply-pocket, the next five in the right pocket of my stinking old trousers, and finally the last five in the left pocket of same, and my sixteen stones will have been sucked once at least in impeccable succession, not one sucked twice, not one left unsucked. It is true that the next time I could scarcely hope to suck my stones in the same order as the first time and that the first, seventh, and twelfth for example, of the first cycle, might very well be the sixth, seventh and sixteenth, respectively, of the second, if the worst came to the worst. But that was a drawback I could not avoid. And if in the cycles taken together utter confusion was bound to reign, at least within each cycle taken separately I could be easy in my mind, at least as easy as one can be, in a proceeding of this kind . . . But however imperfect my own solution was, I was pleased at having found it all alone; yes, quite pleased. And if it was perhaps less sound than I had thought in the first flush of discovery, its inelegance never diminished. And it was above all inelegant in this, to my mind, that the uneven distribution was painful to me, bodily . . . I felt the weight of the stones dragging me now to one side, now to the other. So it was something more than a principle I abandoned, when I abandoned the equal distribution, it was a bodily need. But to suck the stones in the way I have described, not haphazard, but with method, was also, I think, a bodily need. Here then were two incompatible bodily needs, at loggerheads. Such things happen. But deep down I didn't give a tinker's curse about being off my balance, dragged to the right hand and the left backwards and forwards. And deep down it was all the same to me whether I sucked a different stone each time or always the same stone, until the end of time. For they all tasted exactly the same. And if I had collected sixteen, it was not in order to ballast myself in such and such a way, or to suck them turn about, but simply to have a little store, so as never to be without. But deep down I didn't give a fiddler's curse about being without, when they were all gone they would be all gone, I wouldn't be any worse off, or hardly any. And the solution to which I rallied in the end was to throw away all the stones but one, which I kept now in one pocket, now in another and which of course, I soon lost, or threw away, or gave away, or swallowed.

This is the parable of the *Homo scientificus* that I wanted to present. I want to stress two particular things in it. One is the uncanny description of scientific intuition. This is exactly the way Einstein must have struggled to explain the failure of all experiments attempting to demonstrate a motion of the earth relative to the "light-medium," until he very dimly realized that he had to abandon some "principle of trim," the principle of absolute time, and this must have come in some such way as here described. Other people have described intuition in cases where they were able to reconstruct a little of it. Jacques Hadamard, the French mathematician, has written a little book, *An Essay on the Psychology of Invention in the Mathematical Field*, which is a collection of data on this phenomenon and describes how intuition wells up from completely unfathomable depths, first appears in a peculiar guise, and then suddenly breaks out with lightning clarity.

Second, let us look at Molloy's motivation. He certainly is not motivated by the goal of bettering our physical existence or desire for fame or acclaim. Does he do his work "for its own sake," "like art and music"? He describes in detail how his little game "for its own sake" becomes an obsession, beyond all measure of reason. This is not the way you and I do art or music, but it does resemble closely the way the *creative* artist and composers do it. You don't have to look at Beethoven to become convinced of that. Look at any child of five who is obsessed with a creative problem and breaks out in anger and frustration at his failures.

This obsessive fixation picks on anything, quite oblivious of its meaningful content of "revealing the truth about nature" or "bettering our physical existence." It is this quirk of our makeup, this sublimation of other psychic forces, that was delivered by evolution to cave man. More was here delivered by evolution than had been ordered. It carried us from cave man to space man, and may well carry us to our destruction. And why not? The little earthquake we had the other day should have served all of us as a timely reminder, if any reminding is needed, that we are not here to stay, not as individuals, nor as families, nor as nations, nor as the human race, nor as a planet with life on it. There is uncertainty merely as to the time scale.

The point I want to make is this. Man is not only *Homo faber,* the tool maker. The grand edifice of Science, built through the centuries by the efforts of many people in many nations, gives you the illusion of an immense cathedral, erected in an orderly fashion according to some master plan. However, there never was a master plan. The edifice is a result of channeling our intellectual obsessive forces into the joint program. In spite of this channeling, the progress of science at all times has been and still is immensely disorderly for the very reason that there can be no master plan.

So, what could we do if we decided that innovative science is too dangerous? I don't know, but one thing is certain: it would take a lot of manipulation of man—political, economic, nutritional, genetic— if you tried to control *Homo scientificus.*

/Discussion/

QUESTION: Returning to the third question, how can man with the characteristics you just mentioned resist considering implications of his work? This doesn't mean solving them—just considering them.

DELBRÜCK: I understood the question to mean: If I make a discovery, should I consider the implications and maybe not publish it even if it's a basic discovery? I think that it is impossible to foretell the implications. I couldn't agree more that you should *consider* the implications, say, of the genetic manipulation of mankind. You can't help it. It's of the utmost importance. Same with "zero population." I just don't consider this as the same thing as doing science, this business of considering the implications . . . It's something entirely different, as I explained in answer to the second question.

QUESTION: It seems to me that many human beings are subject to neurotic obsession. But it's not clear how we, as scientists, choose problems. It seems to me conceivable that you might choose a problem because somebody tells you that it's an important problem for science. You can get upset about "why the hell can't I solve it" even if you don't care about the problem.

DELBRÜCK: I agree. Science gives the impression of being a magnificant cathedral, an enormous structure—a well-constructed thing, a cathedral built by the continuous effort of many generations through many centuries. Of course it isn't a cathedral because it wasn't planned. Nobody planned the scientific cathedral. To the student it looks as though it were planned. The student gets three volumes of Feynman lectures, 1300 pages of a splendid textbook titled *Organic Chemistry*, and other textbooks, and says "Aha! 150 years ago today they got this far. In the meantime all this was constructed, and now I continue here." My point is, that science is not that at all. Science is primarily playing willfully, and getting obsessed with it, and it is *not* being told: "Here, add your brick on page 1065 and do it properly or we won't give you a Ph. D." Such a student, if you ask him what he is doing, may possibly answer, "I am building a cathedral." More likely, he will say, "I am laying bricks," or even "I am making $4.50 an hour."

QUESTION: Should we not think about how much society should support science?

DELBRÜCK: Oh, I don't want to think about it. It's a very complicated thing. Obviously the high-energy physicists want ever bigger machines that cost a hundred million, billion, etc., and they say the military spend more and the military say if we stop making war the economy will break down. These are all questions that are not very interesting. To me, anyway.

QUESTION: Would you be willing to relax a little bit on your attitude with respect to question 1, the question whether science is beneficial? Would you say this depends on how you define beneficial?

DELBRÜCK: Certainly. If we measure it in terms of energy production or infant mortality, then it's beneficial.

QUESTION: Well, I think it's very difficult to say what *is* beneficial.

DELBRÜCK: Yes, That's why I put a "doubtful" there. I didn't answer "no."

QUESTION: Most of the problem with science is that we don't even know what's beneficial to society.

DELBRÜCK: However, we can hardly evade the fact that the present state of the world leaves much to be desired, and that this is largely a result of the efforts of people like Molloy.

QUESTION: Then one might talk about whether the earlier stage of the world was an awful lot better.

DELBRÜCK: Of course you can. Please do. I don't feel like arguing.

QUESTION: Do you think it is common that scientists proceed in a way that is neurotic? Don't you think that occasionally they do something just because it's interesting?

DELBRÜCK: I didn't mean to use the term neurotic in a derogatory way. Our culture is a product of our neuroses—I mean a product of the diversion of psychic forces from their original function into other directions.

QUESTION: How could you do your research with such a pessimistic attitude? Did you have the same attitude when you started out?

DELBRÜCK: I can't answer that—how I was 40 years ago. If you call it pessimistic, I'm a very cheerful pessimist. I think there's something to be said for the pessimist. It merely means not glossing over some basic facts.

QUESTION: Your picture of a scientist is very personal, so your answer to the first question, "Is science beneficial?", should be "Yes, it's beneficial to the doer." Molloy's pebbles were the same to him as special relativity was to Einstein and the hydrogen bomb to Edward Teller. The difference is that Molloy wasn't going to hurt anybody. Now, if you say that science is beneficial to the scientist because he gets satisfaction from it, and the scientist isn't thinking about the implications, does this imply that somebody else should think about the implications and say, "Molloy, you're OK; Einstein, you're doubtful; Teller, you're out"? Who should make these decisions?

DELBRÜCK: My point was that that's quite impossible. Molloy and Einstein are identical. Einstein worried about relative motion experiments and came up with a solution of the paradoxes which implied, incidentally, an equivalence of mass and energy. This was just as esoteric as shuffling around the sucking stones. I mean that nothing could be more impersonal, impractical, more remote from any social implications than what Einstein did in 1905. To him, anyhow. Later, when the atomic arms race escalated one more round, and Einstein considered that he had been involved in their starting the atom bomb, both by inventing relativity in 1905 and by writing to Roosevelt in 1939, he regretted that he had ever entered science, but I don't think he really had thought about how deeply science is part of human nature. I think discoveries are all potentially equally harmful. Like the circulating of the sucking stones. Maybe Molloy is discovering a principle of permutation or number theory—God only knows the implications of this. Didn't the pictures look like some of the metal organic covalent bond shifting there? Didn't Harry Gray get an inspiration from it for something that's going to be utilized in some horrible contraption in a few years?

QUESTION: Can you draw a distinction in terms of creativity between Einstein thinking up ideas and Edward Teller making bombs—one being playful and the other being purposeful?

DELBRÜCK: I don't have to make this distinction because, if I want to control the bad effects of science, I have to stop Einstein. Why should I try to make a distinction between him and Teller? Teller is an excellent scientist. Although I don't know what he specifically did with the H-bomb, he certainly contributed a great deal to quantum mechanics and chemical physics. So then the question is: Should the scientist stop publishing his science so that the bad appliers won't misuse it? Have a private club? I used to have a slide of a poster I found at MIT, a poster with a quotation from Einstein saying how sorry he was that he had ever, etc., and that if he could start life again he would just become a lighthouse keeper or something like that. Underneath on this poster there was an invitation from somebody saying: "Will you join us in a commune of scientists who will talk among ourselves and not publish anything—just do it by ourselves?" And somebody had scrawled on the side: "Commie." The idea of doing science in a commune and not publishing it seems absurd to me. Why should we get together to follow these pursuits which are not really pleasurable? Molloy had a certain relief and was satisfied that he had found a solution, but the main thing for him was that he was easy in his mind. As easy as one can be in a matter of this kind; suck them turn and turn about. I mean, he had to relieve the uneasiness of his mind. That's where the neurosis comes in—the obsession.

QUESTION: I've been uneasy without being able to articulate it very well, because it seems to me that you say something about the personal obsessions of scientists and the irrelevance of the goal or consideration of a moral principle in their work. I think it's probably only a half-truth. Einstein was a deeply moral man, very concerned. I have a feeling that scientists in their work are buoyed and reinforced by the belief that the answer to question 1 is "yes."

DELBRÜCK: Yes, of course you can be buoyed by the feeling that you've done society good; you can be buoyed by the feeling that you're acquiring fame and prizes. My point is this: Prior to these reinforcements, and more fundamental, even the only, decrepit beachcomber cannot avoid being a scientist, in an obsessive way (exactly the way Einstein was), although both the accessory components are missing. As for Einstein as a young patent clerk in Berne, in 1905, I doubt that he then made a connection between his physics and his responsibilities to society. That's the point I wanted to make. Thank you for making me point it out again. I mean these other components are there, of course, and if you read Jim Watson's book *The Double Helix,* you might think that getting a Nobel prize is everything. However, this would be a grievous misconception.

QUESTION: How many scientists on a desert island would do science for their own benefit?

DELBRÜCK: Even Molloy would. But not for their benefit. He doesn't do it for his benefit. He does it compulsively. I think we all do. No, I take it back. Maybe not. It's a difficult question to answer because most of us are so dulled in our sensitivities that we may be quite incapable of any such complicated argument or reasoning or have the amount of relaxation that this man had. Of course, he had to be able to sit there for hours on the beach and dream up interminable martingales. If you put people on a desert island, probably quite a few of them would dream up interminable martingales and be satisfied with finding something that works.

QUESTION: I wonder if the one place where this parallel between Molloy and other scientists doesn't hold is that Molloy doesn't seem to have any intentions of communicating his results to anyone else. Do you think Einstein would have done his work if he had had no intention of publishing the results? And a personal question: Would you have done science if you had thought no one would be interested in the results?

DELBRÜCK: No, certainly not. In this first essay from which I quoted, by the Scripps girl, it said that scientists are *playing* animals. They not only play alone but they also play together, and if they are not too morose, they actually prefer to play together. And most scientists do prefer to play together. In the case of Einstein, of course, he would never have heard of the paradoxes of prerelativistic physics if he had not been in communication. No, a great joy of the business is communication. All I wanted to point out is the obsessive component of the immediate act of doing science. The channeling of this component toward the erection of a large structure, the institutionalization of it, that is a creation by society and that is something different. That is not a primary characteristic of *Homo scientificus*.

LEE A. DuBRIDGE

*served as Science Advisor to
President Nixon from January 1969
to September 1970. He studied at
Cornell College in Iowa as an
undergraduate and University of
Wisconsin as a graduate student in
physics (Ph.D. 1926). After two
years as research fellow at Caltech,
he joined the faculty of
Washington University in St. Louis.
In 1934, he was appointed professor
of physics and chairman of the
physics department at University
of Rochester. Because of his work in
photoelectric and thermionic
emission and electronics as well as
his administrative ability, during
World War II he went to the
Massachusetts Institute of
Technology to direct the Radiation
Laboratory in its work on radar.
For twenty-three years after the
war, he was deeply involved at the
interface of science and society as
the president of Caltech. He is
currently member of the President's
Science Advisory Committee and of
the Science Advisory Committee of
General Motors.*

CHAIRMAN
John D. Roberts
Professor of Organic Chemistry
Caltech

LEE A. Du BRIDGE

Reflections on Science and Politics

ROBERTS: Two years ago, Lee DuBridge would need no introduction on the Caltech campus—indeed, he was the one who presided over the convocations and introduced the distinguished speakers. Today, there must be quite a few of you who are students that have never seen him before, to whom perhaps he is a legend—the man who, more than any other person, is responsible for the modern Caltech.

Lee came to Caltech at the start of the rising wave of support for science and engineering in universities—his fabulous success in leading World War II radar research at MIT was a big factor in helping that wave get going. He brought to Caltech almost all of its current crop of academic superstars, helped to raise the funds for construction of some thirty buildings, and, on top of this, played an important role in establishing a viable relationship between science and government, and science and community, through dedicated service to almost every important national and local agency.

You might think it was easy to succeed on a rising tide of public support for science such as characterized the DuBridge era at Caltech. In some ways it was, but there were some rough periods. The McCarthy era and the Oppenheimer affair of some twenty years ago had direct and divisive impacts on the campus. More recently, expansion of science departments all over the country led to fantastic pressures on our faculty—men like Murray Gell-Mann and George Hammond often had simultaneous offers from places like Harvard, MIT, Princeton, Stanford, and Berkeley, and so many others from less-favored places that they practically had to have mimeographed replies to be able to keep up with their mail. Lee DuBridge wasn't able to keep everybody here, but his batting average was fabulous and he was always available on short notice to aid embattled division chairmen who needed persuasive eloquence to convince potential defectors that Caltech's future was as promising, indeed more promising, than MIT's or Berkeley's.

Lee left Caltech at near the top of the wave and could have gone on to golden retirement years with a great record of solid accomplishment behind him. Instead of taking this easy route, he chose to enter the eye of the hurricane—to become the Science Advisor to a Republican president, at near the height of disenchantment with the Indochina war, with declining science budgets, with increasing concern of how technology, based on science, has despoiled the environment and brought us to the point of instant annihilation and perhaps destroyed many of the real values of human life. It was a tough assignment, where one could be blamed for much, with little or no real control over what happened. However, I feel that he, not I, should tell you about it.

DUBRIDGE: Thanks very much Jack, for suggesting that I got all the superstars here! However, I see Ernest Swift and Carl Anderson, who were here long before I arrived on this scene. But there are a lot of good friends that came during the days I was here and it's always a pleasure to see them again, and to greet you, faculty, graduates, and undergraduate students.

I purposely entitled my remarks "Reflections on Science and Politics" for I don't have an analytical speech. I just want to talk about a few of the things that have occurred in my lifetime. In this period alone the relation between science and government, science and community, science and public affairs, science and practical affairs, changed radically.

I was an undergraduate student in the years around 1920. At that time, anybody who had used in the same sentence the words "science" and "politics" would have been thought to be slightly cracked. It would have been about as crazy as talking about walking on the moon. And, in 1920, it was. And about the same kind of thing happened. We did walk on the moon. Science did get involved in politics. Nevertheless, as one looks back, one can see developing traces of the relation between science and public affairs, science and government.

These traces became strongly exhibited during World War I. I found when I entered graduate school at the University of Wisconsin that several of the professors had been heavily involved in World War I through scientific research. The head of the National Research Council and one of the leaders of World War I scientific research was our own Robert A. Millikan. In World War I there was not very much time for U.S. science to be mobilized the way it was in World War II. Nevertheless there were, for the short period of time, quite substantial and some quite remarkable scientific research and development projects in the fields of underwater sound, submarine detection, and of chemical warfare (responding to the first German use of chemical warfare in Europe). These activities initiated a lot of other things and immediately following World War I there was a very substantial increase in the tempo of development of American science. Before World War I American science was on a pretty small scale. There were a few brilliant investigators in various fields of science. Probably chemistry was the most active field in this country. Physics was just a stuggling infant. But World War I made a great change. Many kinds of industrial and technological developments were initiated. I think you could say it created the chemical industry, which then really grew in this country after the collapse of the German chemical industry.

But I think most significant was the fact that the head of the wartime scientific effort, George Ellery Hale, then director of Mt. Wilson observatory, and Robert A. Millikan concluded that it was time to extend this same kind of support of science into the world of civilian affairs—into peacetime. And so the National Research Council, created as a wartime mechanism for mobilizing science, became a peacetime supporter and promoter of science in the United States. One of the earliest and most valuable things it did, and Robert Millikan said he thought it was the greatest thing that happened to U.S. science in those days, was the creation of the National Research Council Fellowships. This plan allowed postdoctoral students from various parts of the country to be awarded fellowships on a merit basis and go to study wherever they chose. Caltech, even though it was a very youthful school in the 1920s, attracted a large number of these NRC Fellows. I was fortunate enough to be one of them during the years 1926–1928. I met many physicists here, both graduate students and postdoctoral fellows, who went on to very distinguished careers in science. That's when I first got acquainted with Carl Anderson, who for a few weeks as an undergraduate senior assisted me in my laboratory in the basement of the Norman Bridge Laboratory.

During the period of 1920–1940 there was, relatively speaking, an enormous growth in the status of American science. We caught up, in a sense, to Germany, France, and England, which had been so far ahead of the United States that there was no comparison. By 1940 it was clear that science had developed in this country in a really spectacular way, starting from a pretty small base.

All of this happened almost entirely with support from nongovernment funds. The NRC was a private agency. Even though it advised and worked for the government, the only government funds it received were those to pay the expenses of its various investigations and advisory work. It raised the money for the NRC Fellowships entirely from private sources, primarily from the Rockefeller Foundation. As far as I can recall, the only government agency outside the field of agriculture that put any money into university research was the National Advisory Committee for Aeronautics. Our own Guggenheim Laboratory here received from them what at the time seemed like a very substantial grant—I suppose $20,000 for a year. But in the fields of basic science, physics, chemistry, mathematics, and biology, etc., government support was unknown during that decade.

It seems that it takes a disaster of some sort to change the rate of growth of science. World War II came along and the rate of growth of U.S. science was again sharply changed, to the vast improvement of its quality. During this war the Office of Scientific Research and Development was a civilian agency using government funds. It cooperated with the military, but was not under the military. It operated as a civilian establishment under civilian rules and regulations, receiving funds directly from the Congress as an independent agency. This was contrary to the World War I situation, when Dr. Millikan was not a civilian, but a major in the Army Signal Corps. I won't go into the story of what happened during World War II; I think most of you are familiar with it. Let me now jump to the aftermath and what happened afterward.

Now it was clear on a nationwide basis, as it had not been after World War I, that science had something pretty important to do with the future welfare, prosperity, and security of the country. It would therefore be a good investment for the United States to make a strong effort, this time with substantial government funds, to promote the growth of science, to increase the number of scientists, to ensure the vast improvement of quality of scientific research, development, and teaching that was going on in the country. And so this happened. You all know the story of the expansion of the aircraft and electronics industries (stimulated by the work in electronics and radar and sonar during the war), of the development of computers, of the vast developments of nuclear energy for peacetime purposes as well as nuclear research, and of the beginnings of the work in rockets and later of missiles and space technology. There was tremendous acceleration of effort also in the fields of chemistry and chemical biology. The development and large-scale production of penicillin, for example, was an enormous stimulant to chemical, pharmaceutical, and biochemical industries in their research.

All these industries started broad, extensive, and largely government-supported research and development programs in their various fields, to the vast improvement of U.S. science and U.S. technology. And though we talk about university science as being terribly important to the country, we must remember that a large share of the funds for scientific research and development went to industrial and government laboratories during this period. True, the industries were interested in products, and their work was on the applied level. They were much more interested in those areas of basic science which seemed to have some relevance to their applied goals. But a lot of basic science, as well as an enormous amount of applied science and technology, was stimulated in the years after World War II through government funds.

At the request of President Roosevelt, Vannevar Bush developed, with a distinguished committee, a report on how the lessons of the fostering of research during World War II might be carried over into peacetime civilian research for the greater civilian strength of the country. The result of this study was the famous report "Science: The Endless Frontier." Bush and his colleagues pointed out how critical it was to the future welfare, health, security, economic prosperity, and general welfare of all people, to lay a better base of science and to pursue more energetically the knowledge of nature, so there would be more science eventually to apply to the specific needs of people.

There was created, first, the Atomic Energy Commission to capitalize on the nuclear science and engineering developments during the war. The specific authorization and directive was given to the Atomic Energy Commission to develop basic research in nuclear science and related fields. Substantial programs of university research were thus supported during subsequent years by the AEC. In addition, in their applied work, support was given in both the military and the power fields.

To the Office of Naval Research I give credit for having seen the importance for a military agency to support basic science at the universities of the country. An extensive program was started by the Office of Naval Research to support research primarily in the universities, in astronomy, nuclear physics, solid-state physics, in many fields of basic chemistry, biology, etc., to strengthen the basic science in the country. Later came the National Science Foundation, which carried on basic research as its sole mission. Then came the National Institutes of Health, with rapidly growing support in the years following World War II, and, finally, NASA. I mention these things just to give you a preview of the enormous developments that took place during the period after 1946.

I'd like now to talk about the relation of the scientists to the political activities and problems of the country as they have developed during the past 25 years. I mentioned the creation of the AEC. I guess this is probably the first time scientists got heavily involved in political arguments. The first bill that was introduced in the Congress to create an atomic energy commission frightened many scientists because they thought that it would lead to military control of atomic energy in the postwar days. They did not want this. I think those who worked on the Manhattan District during the war had had enough of military type of organization, and they wanted to be sure that the AEC was a civilian organization. Now I personally think that their fears about this first bill were misplaced. I was involved with Vannevar Bush, James B. Conant, Karl Compton, Robert Oppenheimer, and others in the drafting of that first bill and it was the furthest thing from our minds that anything like military control should be allowed, permitted, or should be fostered. Nevertheless, there was a little paragraph in the bill which provided that officers of the newly formed agency might be retired military officers or might be military officers who took leave of absence from military service. They would serve as civilians, but they could have been military officers. Well, this paragraph scared many scientists. The great battle that followed caused the form of the atomic energy agency that was to be set up to change radically and the present commission form established. I think that if we were doing it over again we would go back to the original bill. A commission of five people has been a pretty impossible administrative operation. Five bosses trying to run an enormous operation has proved politically extremely difficult, administratively almost impossible, and scientifically fraught with some serious and problematical defects. But be that as it may, this was the moment at which a large number of scientists in this country went to the congressional committees, wrote letters to the editor, and made speeches. They declaimed against the potentiality of military control of atomic energy at the end of the war.

A second related effort of scientists in the political arena at that time was the development of proposals and agreements for the international control of atomic energy. There was a strong feeling, I think shared by nearly all scientists, as well as a large segment of the population, that somehow or other this enormous tool of human destruction should be internationalized. This would assure that no single nation or group of nations would have a monopoly of this terrible weapon. Well, those were very strenuous efforts, put out by many scientific people around the country—very conspicuously, by some distinguished Caltech people, Richard Tolman, Robert F. Bacher (who wasn't at Caltech then, but is now), Robert Oppenheimer, Charles Lauritsen. And though the United States failed in persuading the Russians to come into some kind of an international agreement, nevertheless the feeling for it was aroused, mechanisms for it were widely discussed, and active scientific participation in these discussions started then and of course continued actively and intensively down to the present day.

Now I think it's most fitting that Harold Brown is carrying on these same efforts and is leaving next week to take part again in the SALT talks, which is the present, 25-year-later stage of trying to get international agreements on the control of nuclear weapons. I think I've detected in the student newspaper here a couple of criticisms of Harold Brown—that he's been absent a bit. I think we at Caltech should be happy, proud, and glad that he's participating in these SALT talks. If there is to be any hope for an international agreement on the control of nuclear weapons, these SALT talks are absolutely critical. And it is absolutely critical that a man of his knowledge, capacity, good judgment, and devotion to the cause of peace should be the chief scientific advisor to our delegation at these SALT talks. I was delighted when he was named, and I hope that all of you will applaud him for the really self-sacrificing effort.

Well, that was a big political issue in the late 1940s. Another political issue that soon arose was the creation of what became the National Science Foundation. This had been the chief recommendation of the Bush report—that there be created a civilian agency for the sole purpose of supporting basic science in the country, primarily in the universities. Thus basic science would not be supported just as a secondary interest of the military, or as a secondary interest of the Atomic Energy Commission or any other mission agency. One agency would have as its primary function to support basic science and extension of human knowledge. Well, again there was a political battle as to what form this organization ought to take. As a matter of fact, it took several years for all the issues to be ironed out and for a bill finally to be signed by President Truman. He vetoed the first version because he did not think the administrative organization was right. I now think he was probably right, although at the time I didn't think so. Anyway, the National Science Foundation was created after, again, extensive political arguments. So, by 1950 it was clear that scientists were beginning to get a smell of the political world. They've had a lot since.

Actually, there wasn't much opposition to the idea of a science foundation—the argument was solely on the form it should take: the mechanisms and administrative arrangements. I must admit that one strong opponent to the NSF idea was Robert A. Millikan. He was deeply suspicious of the idea of government support of science in the universities and had deep fears of the political involvements that might ensue. I guess he was right! Yet we absolutely could not have had the science progress in this country of these recent years without the National Science Foundation. We've had to take the political problems along with the positive values that resulted from strong government support of science.

During all this time an extraordinary thing was taking place that we physicists and most chemists didn't pay much attention to, but a thing that was critical to the biologists and the people in medicine. That was the growth of the National Institutes of Health. Here was a real political story that I don't know whether anybody's written up or not, but it would be fascinating reading. The National Institutes of Health had a strong leader in Dr. James Shannon. Dr. Shannon had a peculiar ability to get along with congressmen, at least with some congressmen, and he was able to find friends (Senator Lister Hill, I guess, was the chief one) in the Congress who were as strongly committed as he was to the improvement of the health of the American people through better research in biology and medicine and related areas. And so NIH was built up (many people say far too fast, but now I think we all rejoice that it is there) into a billion-dollar-a-year operation, supporting research at universities, within its own laboratories in Bethesda, Maryland, and other places around the country. The result has been a fantastic increase in our knowledge of the nature of life, the nature of biological systems—the physics, the chemistry, the biology of life—and of course this has spilled over in spectacular ways into the fields of medical science. Today there are many health areas in which we no longer have the same type of medical or hospital problems that we had 20 years ago.

It is sometimes said that our hospitals in this country today are of three kinds. The first are the birth-and-death hopsitals, the ones that take care of the arrivals and the departures from this life. These will always be necessary. The second are the "body shops," for the repair of those who go skiing, get in automobile accidents, play basketball too hard, or whatever. We'll always have to have the body shops. The rest of the hospitals are "monuments to ignorance." They're there because we do not know how to prevent and cure the diseases they treat. We don't have any TB hospitals anymore, because we know how to prevent and cure TB. We don't have to have any polio hospitals anymore, because we know how to prevent polio. Just think how nice it would be if we didn't have to have any cancer hospitals, any heart hospitals, any cardiovascular hospitals. We now treat the symptoms and try to keep the patient comfortable. We can do so little about it because we don't understand the basic biology, chemistry, physics, and physiology of the disease itself. And this is why the continuation of the work of the National Institutes of Health is so important.

I think a spectacular example of the importance of NIH is the present situation with regard to cancer. A few years ago there was little hope that we would be able to do much in the field of cancer cures in the next few years. But there have been, through genetics, through biochemistry, through chemistry, and through many other fields, spectacular advances that give at least a cutting edge of an attack on the cancer problem. And that's why President Nixon recently proposed that an additional hundred million dollars in fiscal 1972 be devoted to trying to make more rapid progress in the field of cancer, to capitalizing on the knowledge we've obtained from work in NIH and all the work conducted in universities around the country. I think this is a good political move on the part of the President, but I think it's a very solid and important scientific move and will have important repercussions in strengthening research in all the fields in biology and medicine related to the cancer problem. That's almost the whole of biology and medicine.

The growth of NIH was the result of a strong political alliance between Dr. Shannon, a powerful group of doctors and biologists, and a few senators and congressmen, all of whom were devoted to improving the health of the country. People had some suspicion that a lot of the congressmen who voted for the NIH thought they might die of cancer otherwise and had other, rather personal, reasons. But nevertheless they supplied the money, and while the National Science Foundation was struggling to get its money, the NIH was every year being given more than the president asked. In other words, NSF did *not* have the political punch behind it that the NIH had, and so NSF struggled along with its budget growing rather slowly. Not until after Sputnik did the NSF budget begin a really reasonably rapid rise.

Earlier, I said that it takes a disaster to stimulate progress. And Sputnik was a disaster—at least to the pride and prestige of many American people. The Russians beat us to the first orbiting satellite. A wild wave of denunciation and a wild wave of determination to make things better swept the country in 1957. And again there was a rapid rise in the rate of growth of the support of science by the government. The Sputnik incident had many aftermaths for science, just as World War II.

And so if the 12 years between 1946 and 1958 were years of building a strong science foundation in the country, I can refer to the years between 1958 and 1967 as the Golden Age of Science—golden from the point of view of money. Sputnik stimulated large science appropriations and large requests by President Eisenhower and later other presidents. The Department of Defense, NASA, and NIH benefited, as did the NSF and the AEC. All government agencies were given rapidly rising funds for basic research and for applied research in various critical areas.

One program was begun that would have an important impact. This was a much-enhanced and enlarged program of training of scientists and engineers. In 1946 there probably were not more than a dozen or 20 institutions in the United States that could be said to offer first-class Ph.D. work in the basic sciences. And the number who could be admitted to those institutions, while growing, was still inadequate for foreseeable demands for scientists and for engineers. With the development of the NASA program it became clear that a large and increasing demand for scientists and engineers was in the offing. Large government funding was provided for fellowship and traineeship programs. Thus the number of graduate students working on research projects was greatly expanded during those years.

And then, too, an awareness developed that there ought to be many more first-class institutions giving good graduate work in the science and engineering fields. And so largely through the NSF, special funds were allocated to strengthen the second-level institutions—those below the first 20 but which had the possibility of improving their programs. And now, although the original 20 are still the top 20, there are certainly another 50 institutions which have vastly improved their graduate programs in the science and engineering fields in the last 10 or 15 years.

In 1958, President Eisenhower created the office of Science Advisor to the President and later the Office of Science and Technology to back him up. James R. Killian, Jr., was the first Science Advisor. He brought to the central part of government a topnotch group of scientists, some on a full-time basis, many others serving on a variety of advisory committees, to work directly with the President on the problems related to the fostering of American science and technology. This greatly strengthened the political position of science in the government. The Science Advisor was created as really a very high level position in the government—just below the cabinet level. There are only probably four or five out of the hundreds of members of the White House staff that have the same status, the same level in government, the same executive appointment that the Science Advisor has. So he became one of a pretty small group of senior advisors to the President of the United States. Different presidents use advisors in different ways, but the status is always there. And believe me, in Washington status symbols are terribly important. This meant that the Science Advisor was listened to in the halls of Congress. He was listened to in a variety of other political circles. Science finally found a voice that it had not had at all in the previous years.

And so, during the period from the end of World War II until 1967, the funding of university scientific research grew from essentially nothing to $2 billion a year. For many years between about 1950 and 1965 the rate of growth was 21 percent per year, compounded. So you see, it grew like a bacterial colony. There were those who extrapolated that curve to see when it would exceed the gross national product. With the GNP growing at 4 percent per year, science funding growing at 21 percent per year, you can do a little logarithmic plotting and figure it out yourself. Clearly this couldn't go on forever.

Then in 1967 came the reaction. The end of the Golden Age. What happened? Well, the story is so complicated that it's impossible in the few minutes I want to take here to really recite it. I'm sure most of you know much of it anyway. Senator Hill died, Dr. Shannon retired, and the political support behind the National Institutes of Health leveled off sharply. The Apollo program reached the peak of its spending about 1967. NASA no longer needed the huge $6 billion-a-year appropriations, and so no matter what attitude the country would have had then, its appropriations would have certainly declined. But with the attitude of the country they declined even faster, from nearly $6 billion a year to a little over $3 billion now.

And then of course the horrible situation in Viet Nam grew, became of more concern throughout the country, throughout the government, throughout the Congress, and throughout the Administration. It had all kinds of reactions, some understandable, some a little strange. One, of course, was the reaction against the military support of science, even the military support of basic science in universities—the same kind of science that the Science Foundation was supporting. There was a reaction against the use of military funds for the support of any science. I think the reaction was an ill-conceived reaction, but it was there, and it certainly had a strong effect on the economics.

Then, too, there was the growing feeling of, "Well, yes, science has performed a lot of miracles, we got to the moon, we got the atomic bomb, but science isn't all that great. It hasn't cured cancer, it hasn't solved the problems of our environment, it hasn't solved the urban problem, the racial problem, it hasn't made everybody rich. Science isn't so good after all." Well, I believe these things were strongly expressed, in newspaper editorials (especially in the eastern press), in many letters to the editor, in many letters to congressmen, and in many speeches on the floor of Congress and on platforms around the country. People said, "We have overrated science all these years, it isn't so hot after all. Not only that but it's making things worse instead of better. Look at the smog, and look at DDT, and look at eutrophication, and look at some other things." Well, this attitude, believe me, gets rapidly reflected in the halls of Congress and even in many parts of the Administration. There was a growing fear related to the distrust of technology and science: "What will they do next that will bring terrible tragedy and trouble to the people of the world?"

Another factor was certainly the troubles on the campus. This created very unhappy reactions in the halls of Congress and many parts of the Administration: "If the universities can't keep their house in order, why should the government give them any money?" And there were many many moves to reduce the appropriations for any purpose to universities just because the students misbehaved and the administration wasn't able to keep them in line.

And so, for these and many other reasons which coincidentally arose in the years 1967–1968, the academic research funding leveled off. It didn't really decline, taken as a whole, but since inflation was still going ahead, the net science that could be bought declined 10, 15, 20 percent maybe, over a period of three or four years.

Well, it was just at this unhappy period of American history of science that I took the journey to Washington. Just a little over two years ago now. And the first question was: "What's the Nixon administration going to do about this matter?" Well, the new President was faced with two serious problems. First, the previous administration had already prepared the budget for fiscal 1970, which had to be submitted to Congress early in 1969. There was very little the new administration could do about any radical, sweeping changes in that budget. It would have taken six months of reworking to come up with a new one which was very much different. So only some tinkering with it was possible.

The first tinkering that the President felt had to be done was to bring down the deficit. The deficit had piled higher and higher during the previous years. Although President Johnson made strenuous efforts to reduce it in his last year and reduce it in the 1970 budget which he prepared, Nixon felt that still additional reductions were necessary. Hence a terrible budget crunch was the first thing that was faced. The budget crunch simply forced cuts in practically every agency and department of government, practically every activity except the uncontrollable ones. I discovered there are many expenses that even the President or the Congress can't control, for example the interest on the national debt, social security, medicare, and many other expenses which have their own built-in formulas, which cannot be changed. Therefore, although Nixon did propose in fiscal 1970 a moderately good increase in the budget of the National Science Foundation, it was one of the very few agencies that got any proposed increase in the Administration's budget. Unfortunately Congress didn't see it that way, and instead of increasing the NSF budget as the President requested, by about $40 million, they cut it by about $60 million. The House tried to cut it by $80 million, the Senate was a little more generous and only cut it by 40. They compromised at a $60-million cut from the amount that had been requested.

This was bad enough, but it was compounded by the fact that a cut in the Department of Defense research budget was also made. Since the Department of Defense had been supporting substantial and excellent work in the universities, that was a real cut in available funding. And then to add to the problem, Senator Mansfield introduced his famous amendment saying that the Department of Defense could not spend money for research that wasn't directly connected with and pertinent to a military mission or purpose. This wiped out a lot of good scientific work that the Department of Defense had been supporting. With NSF's cut, it was not able to take over any of that work.

Now just as I was leaving Washington, the fiscal 1972 budget was being prepared and the picture there was substantially different, substantially better. The Administration decided last fall that in view of the economy of the country a balanced government budget was not possible. Indeed it was not desirable and therefore a deficit budget could be prepared again, as had not been allowed in fiscal 1970 and fiscal 1971. This meant, after the arguments had ceased (mostly after I left), that there was a $110-million increase proposed for the National Science Foundation. It was really more than that because the NSF was relieved of some of its responsibilities, such as the Sea Grant Program, which made this an even larger actual increase. One hundred million dollars was also recommended for the cancer problems I've already mentioned. Many other R and D programs were increased. They are mostly small in size, but they may be very important for the future, such as new funding for environmental research, for urban and transportation problems, and for urban housing and similar problems. Even though the research funds for some of these new agencies are small, a few million dollars, a 50 to 75 percent increase—100 percent in some cases—is about all they can take in one year. Management skills have to be built up in order to rapidly increase the ability to manage funds. But these are on the way up and a considerable boost is given in the proposed 1972 budget. I was glad to see also that with the re-creation of the Bureau of Budget into the Office of Management of Budget and the appointment of George Schultz as head of that, and Casper Weinberger, a wonderful Californian, as head of the budget part, a whole new attitude appeared in that office in regard to the support of scientific research in universities. So I have the feeling that we've turned the corner and that appropriations hopefully will follow these budget proposals.

But it isn't all that easy, maybe, because Congress is still there. They can still cut the budget as much as they please, or increase it as much as they please. They still have the fears that they get from the rest of the country about the impacts of science and technology, about the problems on the campus, about whether we shouldn't be putting our money into other things. "Hasn't science gone too far, is it really all that valuable when we can think of other things that need to be done that science can't attack, etc., etc?" The best we can hope for, of course, is a return to a growth rate, not a decline rate, of the support of science. Certainly we expect a smaller growth rate than the 21 percent that we enjoyed during the Golden Age. How much of a growth rate? This, of course, remains to be seen. It will take maybe a 5 percent growth rate to match inflation; it will take maybe another 2 or 3 percent to match the actual rise in costs of scientific research as it gets more sophisticated, therefore more difficult and more expensive. But there is some hope. The basic science budget in 1972, as proposed by President Nixon, is about 13 percent above the 1971 budget, which is a fairly healthy rise and will be at least double the inflationary rise. There are also some changes in emphasis and content in the program. This is understandable and reasonable. Any program should be reviewed every few years and new directions sought that are pertinent to the times.

The saddest thing I think that is happening is that, because of the anticipated reduction of demand for scientists and engineers, particularly in industry, to some extent in universities, the programs for training more graduate students have been sharply tapered off. This has resulted largely from the actions of the Office of the Management of the Budget. It has analyzed, I think with a good deal of skill, the projected needs for Ph.D.s in engineering and science in the next few years and it has come to the conclusion that the present rate of production and particularly the present rate of increase of production (we're producing 10 percent more scientists every year than we did the year before) is too large. At the same time the number of scientists being produced each year is 10 percent per year of the total number. Well, maybe this is wrong, but the questions is: What is the proper level? The trouble is that nobody can really firm that up because we don't know what the demand will be in 5, 6, 7, or 8 years from now when the present students are getting their Ph.D.s, are completing their training, and are ready for jobs. I think it's risky to cut back too much on the training of graduate students. And yet it's happening. We only hope that somehow the slack can be taken up in future years. Perhaps universities can find ways to use research funds for training graduate students.

Well, a few words now about what I was supposed to talk about originally: What is the responsibility of the scientist and engineer, particularly the young ones who are coming along? There are going to be political battles on all these things that I've mentioned. What should we be doing about it?

Well, to the young scientist, let me say here, your first responsibility is very clear, and let me emphasize it with all my power. The first responsibility of a scientist is to be a good scientist. If you aren't that, then everything else is lost. If we don't have good scientists in this country, we might as well forget it. The reason science has contributed so greatly to the country, the reason it's grown so greatly and improved in quality, is because we have such a host of wonderful minds who have studied and worked in science during these many years.

And related to that is a second piece of advice: Attack significant problems. Notice I did not say relevant problems. The word "relevance" is the enemy of lots of good basic science because you must ask yourself, "Will this cure cancer, will this cure our urban problems?" If you're working on problems in basic physics or chemistry or biology, you don't know, you haven't the faintest idea of what the knowledge gained is going to be in the first place, and what its application will possibly be in the second place. So relevance too insistently applied (as in the Mansfield amendment) is the enemy of good basic science, the search for knowledge.

It's *not* the enemy of applied science, because that's what applied science is. It's seeking to apply the knowledge you've gotten in basic science to particular problems important to our society, whatever they might be. Recall as much as you can while you're being a good scientist and working on significant problems (significant in the sense that they contribute to the advance of science)—recall and emphasize to your friends, to your students, the contributions of science to human welfare. We hear so much about the adverse effects of science that you might think that the people 200 years ago were so much better off than we are today, physically, mentally, spiritually. But think back to 200 years ago, when science had just started and compare the nature of an ordinary human being, the way he lived, the things he put up with, the kind of life he led, with what we have today. A large fraction of the population at that time, of course, was slaves or serfs. That's not true any more. And think of all the other ways in which knowledge and the application of knowledge for the betterment of the human condition has greatly advanced the human condition now, as compared to any time in human history. And understanding nature has been the essential element in the advance of human welfare during the last 200 years. As one understands nature, one can then open up new areas for applying the understanding to develop the mechanisms, the techniques, the technologies, that will do for us the things that we want to do. The good things we want to do. And it's up to us to see that we use them for the good things that we want to do. But you can't do good things with science if there isn't the science available.

Finally, I think it's been evident from what I said that the public understanding of science, the understanding by newspaper editors, writers of letters to the editor, people in business, lawyers, congressmen, by politicians in all levels of all governments, is going to be essential if there's going to be a spirit which says that the extension of knowledge is important for the human condition, for the human race, and for the outlook of the human spirit. If we can promote that gospel, we may be sure that the reversal in the fortunes of science will be a real one in years to come.

/ Discussion /

QUESTION: Could you tell us more about interaction between your office and Congress?

DUBRIDGE: Yes. That's a long, complicated story, I'm afraid. Of course, the Science Advisor reports to the President. As Science Advisor he has no connection with Congress at all. But, as it has been arranged, he also wears another hat. He heads a statutory office established by the Congress, the Office of Science and Technology. As director of this office he does report to Congress. He has to get from Congress a budget for the Office, for example, and he can be called to testify on matters pertinent to the activities of the Office. So it's a somewhat delicate position to be in. One must work closely with the President on matters of science in things that are coming ahead in the future. While the President is just evolving his ideas, his policy on them, one has to be in there early to give him the facts, give him the opinions of competent scientists and engineers on the scientific aspects of the issue. These things certainly cannot be made public, cannot be divulged to Congress until the President's policies have been formulated. And once he's made up his mind and announced his policy, then of course the Science Advisor supports that policy even though he may have had some reservations about it. As a member of the President's team, he stays a member of the President's team. That doesn't mean he has to lie about his own feelings, obviously. But he should in general either keep quiet or else support what the President has to say, even though the technical facts as he sees them may be against the decision. The President considers many other facts, economic, political, international, etc., which go far beyond the science and technology. Science and technology are usually a small part of the big decisions that the president himself has to make.

Nevertheless we did have many Congressional contacts by every member of the staff (there are about 20 professional staff members in OST). Every member has a particular area of interest, a particular field of competence—geology, physics, biology, etc. He gets acquainted with the congressmen that are on the committees that are dealing with appropriations on legislation in that area. He prepares testimony, often testimony for the Director to use. And there is a great deal of interaction. But with a staff of 20 people, of course, the interaction isn't on that large a scale. It's usually friendly, well informed, and fairly intimate, particularly with the staff of the congressional committees. These staff members are the most powerful people in Congress. As I found out, it's the staff of a committee that really guides the chairman as to the direction in which his committee is going to go. And they're very smart people, some of them, and working with them proved to be very fruitful. So there is a great deal of back and forth on an informal basis, but formally the Science Advisor advises the President, the cabinet members, and the White House staff people and does not attempt directly to advise Congress.

QUESTION: What about the members of the President's Science Advisory Committee, do you think that they should keep quiet about the way they feel?

DUBRIDGE: We had some arguments on that score and we never settled it. There were those on the Science Advisory Committee who felt, yes, as long as we were to be in the President's confidence, as long as he has referred confidential matters to us and listened to us in a confidential, private way, that we should not afterward, making use of the information and the ideas that we had got from that process, then go out and oppose the President's policy on scientific grounds. But many members didn't go along with that idea and some fellows followed their own.

QUESTION: Many of the schools that began expanding their graduate programs after World War II with government encouragement have had their funds dry up recently. Could you comment on their future? Do they contribute to diversification?

DUBRIDGE: Many new Centers of Excellence have been disappointed, and are going to be more so because the funds have been removed now and places that have just started to develop are going to be unable to continue. There've been some good results, some places have really come far along, often at the cost of the scientists they "swiped" from Caltech, MIT, Harvard, and the rest. Maybe they spread the talent a little bit but it's not too bad.

As to diversification, you know, there are millions of significant things in science to be done. There are so many problems, so many areas of ignorance, that there's no reason why two people have to do the same thing unless they do it for confirmation or together. But the styles run in a certain direction and you feel you're out of the significant areas of chemistry unless you're doing chemical dynamics, say. Diversification, of course, is absolutely essential. If you look back, look at the diversification there has been over these many years, the fields of science, the problems of science that were never thought of 20 years ago, that have grown. And that's the real problem for people like you in universities: to look at the significant areas in science, where we are lacking in knowledge, the things that would really help us to understand nature better and get those significant problems widely examined.

QUESTION: Do you feel that scientists have any obligation to control the use of science for evil purposes?

DUBRIDGE: Scientists control evil people? How can they do that? Scientists seek knowledge, and as they apply the knowledge, naturally they owe it to their conscience to apply it in the most useful and constructive way. But to prevent a particular piece of knowledge from being used by evil people? I do not see how a scientist can. He might declaim against it, but how he can stop it is something I'm unable to understand. Furthermore, for every piece of knowledge that's been used in a bad way, that same piece of knowledge, I bet you, has been used in a thousand good ways. I think you could give many examples. So, you discover nuclear energy—is that good or bad? Well, it was a great scientific and later a great technological achievement. My guess is that, in the long run, it will make life better for more people than it will make life worse for, provided first we can go ahead with this international control, for which I'm still very hopeful. But you don't even know what the results of an experiment are going to be when you start it. You can't possibly then tell how it's going to be used, if at all. Even when it's been out and confirmed and understood for many years, still someone can pop up with a new idea about how to use that kind of thing for something wrong—the problem is people then, not evil scientists.

QUESTION: There is quite an amount of disillusionment that I and other young scientists feel about the role of science in the community and I would appreciate your comments on the implications of this disillusionment for the future.

DUBRIDGE: Well, I don't know where to start. Certainly a lot of nonsense on this subject has been declaimed by important people (a lot of nonsense as I view it) but a lot of good sense also. I'm particularly worried about the nonsense in the environmental field. When I went to Washington the first task President Nixon assigned me was to develop a mechnaism for improving the government activities in environment protection. Suddenly, after not having had much to do with that subject in my life, I got interested and started looking into the problem to see what the government could do. We organized a cabinet committee and we began discussing what could be done in Agriculture, Interior, HUD, DOD, and NSF in the environmental field. Then the whole field blew up and everybody became an ecologist—some of them with the wildest ideas. They thought ecology was a new discovery, you know, that had just been made yesterday. They didn't realize that ecology had been studied by ecologists for many, many years. There were many things known about ecology that were now ignored, were not reexamined, not put in perspective. Is DDT a good or bad thing for the world? It saved half-a-billion human lives and destroyed quite a few pelicans and pigeons and salmon and other things. Now how do you balance the two? And this is a terrible thing that the people of this country have to face: Which do you prefer, the lives of half-a-billion human beings who would otherwise have died of malaria, yellow fever, and all the other insect- and lice-borne diseases, or the fact that certain kinds of fish and birds are adversely affected? Well, if you go from one thing to another throughout the whole field of ecology, you always find a question: What are the balances between the good and bad thing? Phosphates weren't put together with soap just for the hell of it or to make Lake Erie stink. They were put there by responsible scientists and chemical engineers to convert soap into a better cleaning agent. And since we'd be completely out of tallow if we depended solely on soap now and didn't have detergents, it was a lifesaving thing that they invented detergent. And nobody's found a substitute for phosphate in detergent that's satisfactory. Various ones have been tried and seem to have worse environmental implications than phosphate itself. And phosphate is a small problem in the country as a whole. Even in Lake Erie it's only a small piece of the problem. But people say "abolish phosphate, abolish DDT," as though a sudden abolition of the thing that was developed and tried and worked over many years was either economically or healthwise possible or desirable. Well, the point is that one should look at all the substitutes for DDT that can be developed. There are many coming along, but, you know, some of them may be just as harmful as DDT when they're used on a large scale. It's going to take a long time to find out, and so I think we'd better go slow in throwing away things that we know are going to be of enormous value to human beings before we throw in something of very doubtful future benefit.

Well, I don't know if this is relevant to what you say or not, but I think this confusion in the environmental field is something that the young scientists should carefully look at: What *are* the facts about these various things in which so much argument is being stirred up now in the environmental field? There are facts to be found out and I'm delighted that there is an environment laboratory starting at Caltech; they'll really find out about some of these things so that we can base our actions on knowledge and experience and not on emotion. And the same is true in so many other fields of the application of science to social problems—it's a terribly complicated field and we're not going to change social problems overnight by just a few scientists changing their line of attack: although many of them should, if they desire, and have the talents, move into the areas in which application can have a foreseeable social benefit. We've always had scientists, and we've had applied scientists and engineers, and we always, I hope, will. By and large, in the country as a whole, far more money and more people go into the applied areas than into the basic ones. It takes a special kind of quirk of the mind, a special kind of talent, to do significant basic science. And I would dread to think that many people with that peculiar and very valuable talent would not use it to its fullest. There are plenty of people who can do the applied work, many more than can do significant basic work in science itself. Don't you believe that, George? Not that it's any easier. You're shaking you head as though you didn't like what I said.

GEORGE HAMMOND: Applied science is *hard!*

DUBRIDGE: Yes, and so is basic work.

QUESTION: I feel the idea of a pecking order between applied and basic sciences should be done away with.

DUBRIDGE: I didn't intend to imply a pecking order, I just said the talents and interests were different. I don't think there's a pecking order between a physician and a physicist. They're just different kinds of people with different kinds of talents and interest. I wouldn't hold one above the other, nor would I put the applied scientist above the basic scientist or vice versa. But I do think that without saying it's a better or superior kind of talent, that it is a different kind of talent that leads one to work imaginatively in the applied field as compared to what leads on to work imaginatively in the basic field.

QUESTION: Since the government encourages and supports graduate students, doesn't it have a responsibility to find jobs for them?

DUBRIDGE: No. I think the government has a responsibility for promoting science and engineering and the welfare of the country and in that process it will need a lot of scientists and engineers, at least it has in the past. But because it's contributed to the stipend of a graduate student I do not believe that the government is then responsible for getting that graduate student a job when he gets through. It's a private-enterprise business.

Now, we just had a talk with the President the other day (he met with the Science Advisory Committee) and he is terribly worried about the fact that too many scientists and engineers are not being fully employed or are not being employed at all. He's asked the Science Avisory Committee to study hard to see if they can come up with some ideas that will relieve the situation. He feels a responsibility. But I think really one should not say, "The Government has to get me a job because the Government paid for my education." You see, the whole rationale behind putting money into traineeships and fellowship on the part of NASA, and AEC, and DOD was: "We need ["we" = the agency] more scientists, we're not getting enough of them. The universities, Harvard, Caltech, etc., are getting all of them and there aren't enough left over for us; therefore, let's train some more." So the whole rationale for increasing the funding of graduate study by stipends to students was the need of the agencies for more scientists. And then as NSF looked at the picture as a whole, it also saw the need, not for itself but for the country, of more scientists, and so it pushed ahead. Well, now when NASA didn't need any more scientists, they abolished their traineeship program. That's a natural reaction. If you were in charge of a budget that was limited and you were paying for the training of scientists and you didn't need them, why of course you'd quit. So did the DOD and AEC and so did the rest. NSF has struggled hard to keep its program alive. Its fellowship program is being maintained. But the administration, the Office of Management of the Budget, felt that the traineeship program should be cut back because, as I said, we were producing scientists at an increasing rate. Already it was hard to see how the production could be absorbed in the next ten years.

QUESTION: Isn't it irresponsible to train scientists you do not need?

DUBRIDGE: Well, I would say that, too. You can't make a day-by-day decision on this. You can tell how many automobiles to produce because you know how many sold last week. You know how many to produce next week. But with scientists, you start producing a scientist today, he becomes a scientist in six years, plus two more years as a postdoc. Eight years have gone by and you have no idea what the demand is going to be then. So I think one shouldn't pre-guess the future too much. That's happened too often in the past.

H.D.　　　　C.P.　　　　G.H.　　　　N.D.

NORMAN R. DAVIDSON

*is professor of chemistry at Caltech.
He received his B.S. at the
University of Chicago in 1937, his
B.Sc. at Oxford in 1938, and his
Ph.D. at the University of Chicago
in 1941. He did research for the
government during World War II,
and joined the Caltech staff in 1946.
His principal research has been in
physical and inorganic chemistry,
especially the study of very fast
reactions and the study of complex
ion formation. Currently, his major
interest is the study of the DNA
molecule with the electron
microscope. He is a member of the
National Academy of Sciences.*

HARRY G. DRICKAMER

is a professor of chemical engineering and physical chemistry at the University of Illinois. He received all his college training at the University of Michigan, B.S.E. (1941), M.S. (1942), Ph.D. (1946). He has been a member of the faculty of Illinois since that time, serving as Head of the Chemical Engineering Division from 1955 through 1958. His experimental work has increased our knowledge of chemistry at high pressures and of the electronic structure of solids. He is a member of the National Academy of Science.

GEORGE S. HAMMOND

is Arthur Amos Noyes Professor of Chemistry and Chairman of the Chemistry and Chemical Engineering Division at Caltech.
(See "John Chemist," p. 18.)

CHAIRMAN

Cornelius J. Pings
Provost, Professor and
  Executive Officer of Chemical Engineering
Caltech

NORMAN R. DAVIDSON,
HARRY G. DRICKAMER,
GEORGE S. HAMMOND

The Future of Chemisty

PINGS: We're here today to discuss the future of chemistry—if any. The format is to be one involving brief opening remarks by three distinguished chemists, commentaries from each upon the remarks of the other two, if they so desire, and then the opening of the forum for comments and questions from those of you in the audience. I believe that the rules of engagement agreed upon in advance stipulated about 10 minutes for the prepared remarks of each, and I'll attempt to moderately enforce that and otherwise keep order as necessary. Your organizer has put together a distinguished panel of speakers: two local experts, and another flown in from the Midwest. All are distinguished chemists and/or chemical engineers. All are members of the National Academy of Sciences. They will speak in the order of Hammond, Davidson, and Drickamer. I think really little introduction is needed on the first two, Hammond of course is the chairman of this distinguished Division, Davidson is responsible for the chemistry component of that. Dr. Drickamer is in residence this week as the fourth Lacey Lecturer and will give that lecture tomorrow afternoon. He is Professor of Chemical Engineering and Physical Chemistry at the University of Illinois.

HAMMOND: I'll try to speak briefly (this is not one of my habits) and I'll try to talk about what I really think is likely to happen in chemistry in the fairly near future. Two kinds of prediction are damned easy to make. One is a prediction of how things are likely to have changed over a period of time like 100 years or a couple of hundred years—these are very easy, because you can often see that in the long run very great changes are likely to occur. Predicting this in a somewhat qualitative nature is simple. Also, if you're completely wrong, you're dead by the time it turns up and everyone's forgotten, so it's pretty safe. The other kind of prediction that's easy is what's likely to happen next week or next year, and that's such a simple extrapolation from what's here now that it's also pretty simple to do with, I think, reasonable accuracy. Really tough things are what's going to happen in 5 to 15 years, because there, great changes that you see coming may not have time to begin or may not be noticeable over this period. Also, with decent luck you're likely to be alive and people may remember what you said.

My first prediction is that in the foreseeable future (in a few generations) it's quite possible that the traditional disciplines of science will have been mixed up, redefined, and done differently. Chemistry won't exist explicitly, nor will physics. However, I don't think this is going to happen in a big hurry, and so over the short range of the next couple of decades, chemistry is likely to still stay chemistry. For better or for worse, I think this is likely to happen. The rate at which people change their ways of thinking about things and doing things is probably too slow for something that's been ingrained in the society for well over 100 years to change to the extent that it does not appear the same.

Other predictions have to do with areas of activity within chemistry or chemical science. First, in research: I think the style of research done in various kinds of chemistry probably will change quite a lot within the next 10 years. We'll probably see a lot more changes in the general method of approach than have occurred in the last 10 years. The last 10 years have been very important in that we've learned to do many of the things that people tried to do during the previous decade, a whole lot better, with new tools, new precision, new thinking, etc., and so I think some switch in orientation will occur. There'll be more emphasis on doing new things, answering new questions, than there will be in solving some of the questions that have been classic for the past 20 years. I even think that it's likely that there will be an increased movement toward obliteration and slow redefinition of the subdisciplines within chemistry. This is something that can happen a lot more rapidly than the remapping of all science. And I don't know whether or not the change will be to say that chemists are structurers, people in dynamics, synthetic chemists, or something else, but I do think that there is a very significant turning away from the very classical subdisciplines as we've known them.

Second area, chemical industry: I think there will be quite a lot of change in the chemical industry. Just how it'll occur I don't know, but as I've said quite a number of times, I think that the missions of industrial chemistry have not changed a whole lot during a period when there's been great development. People keep saying, "What we need is a new nylon," and so they invent nylon over and over and over again. They get another new fiber, maybe using beautiful polymer chemistry, but I think probably nothing equivalent to a new nylon will occur in competition with nylon. It really can't, because nylon has been there. And I think that this kind of philosophy will slowly either sink into the traditional chemical industry or else we will probably see arising slowly new chemically based industries. If so, then the traditional chemical industries, like Monsanto and du Pont will, in fact, become commodity industries, and the real action in new industrial chemistry will be the newcomers. And probably this new industry will place less emphasis on turnover of masses of material, which has been characteristic in the recent past. Questions such as how much of a thing can you produce, how many pounds of it can you sell, will be asked less often, simply because this would be consistent with other societal trends. The society is beginning to worrry about masses of stuff that we pass through our hands and process. If you'll remember Norman Brooks' seminar . . . he made a strong point of that.

Government research is a separate area on which I'd like to comment directly. I think that, in one form or another, chemical scientific research is likely to become relatively more important in government's own laboratories than has been true in the near past, simply because the big things in volume of dollars and also in the people involved, in the near past, have been in militarily related research, in aerospace industry, and to some extent in development of new electronics industry to support the military and to support aerospace. These things are going to be decreased. It's almost inevitable that the government itself is going to stay in scientific research. As one kind of thing is turned down, another is likely to be turned up. I don't think it's all going to go into health-related science, because that's already fairly large, but I believe that among the likely candidates will be some kind of chemically related science. It's likely that this will start out sounding as though it's all environmental and turn into other things as people branch out.

The fourth area is education. I think there's going to be tremendous change in chemical education during the next 10 years. Not primarily because of the kind of gas that I've been emitting the last several years about chemical education, but simply because chemical education is a part of a very large system, general education, which *is* going to undergo, and is undergoing, enormous changes. Whether change in chemistry should take place is almost irrelevant.

It will. There will be less emphasis on the goodness of great numbers of students, in chemistry and elsewhere, because as a nation we face the fact that we've probably overproduced intellectual snobs. Thirty years ago that type had a unique and valuable role, but now we have more of them than needed at the moment and this is something that the nation as a whole will struggle with. There will be many experiments with new styles in education. For example, we may even discover that the lecture, which is, of course, a heritage from the time before there were books, is not necessarily the greatest way on earth to communicate. I don't know. But there'll be a good deal of playing with style and chemistry will be a part of it, although perhaps not a leading part. Education of all kinds will become a lot less homogeneous, simply because we have overproduced too many people who are educated too similarly. Education will clearly become less paternalistic. The way I think of the future, I don't think of whether or not the paternalistic style of education is better or worse, I simply see it changing and I tend to think about adapting usefully to the change. As chemists I think we should do this at least as fast as the large system. I'd like to see us do it faster but I suspect this won't happen because chemists on the whole seem to be pretty conservative.

Other random predictions: First, there are going to be a lot more women in chemistry because I think that women's libbers are really going to make their point. In some ways I like this. I don't know what'll come of it but I expect that it's a change that will be very apparent 15 years from now. Another prediction I make is that organizations of chemists, such as the ACS, will *not* become protective societies like the AMA, as many chemists are now recommending. For various reasons I think this is not appropriate. Chemistry is a different kind of business and it wouldn't work as well. Also, the AMA is in some ways so nauseating that I think it will probably be destroyed during this period of time, and consequently the chances of some other group of professional people becoming more like that are pretty small.

I have one last thing to say which is not a prediction, simply a hope. I wish I could predict that the style of chemical science would become a lot more realistic in self-appraisal. What we need is a good deal less sacredness in our view of ourselves and a desire for people to view us—a good deal less feeling of total responsibility for everything that happens in the world. In fact, I think that the philosophy expressed and then stubbornly adhered to by Max Delbrück a couple of weeks ago is very desirable. Max stood here and insisted that no matter how much you want it, I'm not going to take myself quite that seriously. That was a very important message. I think that it makes Max and his science better. It certainly does not detract from the operations of the society to take that view. I think we need a lot more of Delbrück, probably a lot less of Woodward and the Woodward aura, and probably less of the violent social mission that we hear fairly frequently expressed. It's a very laudable kind of ambition, but I suspect that it's not going to be overall effective in us. I agree with Max: We're not that good that we have to worry completely about how we feel about things—it doesn't make all that much difference.

DAVIDSON: I started to write out this 10-minute speech (I never do it for a 40-minute lecture), and it sounded terrible. One paragraph was platitudinous, and the next one struck me as likely to get me lynched. So instead of that I've written out a series of more or less disconnected statements. I'm still likely to ultimately emit platitudes or things that are going to get me lynched, but at least you're not going to criticize me for not having an organized systematic presentation. It's not *supposed* to be an organized, systematic presentation.

My first topic is the economic future of chemistry. Here I'll emulate Dr. Delbrück and summarize my projections in a table (Table 1). The economic future of chemistry is very bleak right now. The guys who were here the last few days told us essentially that the chemical industry isn't hiring anybody. And the signals I picked up from listening to these guys are that the probable rate of hiring in the *chemical industries* over the next decade, or something like that, is going to be less than half—perhaps a half to a quarter—of what

Table 1

Estimates by Allan M. Cartter of New Faculty Required to Maintain* Quality, and New Doctorates Available

Chemistry	New faculty with Ph.D. needed	New Ph.D.s*
1965	505	1439
1970	492	2030
1975	578	2290
1980	475	2888
1985	−37	n.a.

*A.M. Cartter, A New Look at the Supply of College Teachers, *Educ. Rec.* (Summer 1965), p. 267.

it has been in the great years. *Government support:* The latest signals are that that's going to be up some from the recent bleak years, and just how that affects the overall picture, I don't know. *Teaching* is bleak. This is true in the long run, although maybe not in the shorter term. These are data from the 1966 Cartter report. These are his predictions of new faculty with Ph.D.s that will be needed. And I guess the main point is that this is essentially constant through 1980, and then because of population trends or something it becomes negative. Now, according to George Hammond, half these teachers are going to be female and the demand for male teachers is accordingly cut in half. These were Cartter's projections based on the trends at the time as to the number of Ph.D.s that were going to be produced and I guess this is about right. Presumably there will be some feedback and this growth in the number of Ph.D.s isn't going to go on. I suppose in a certain sense that his prediction of the constancy in the demand for faculty for the next 10 years can be regarded as modestly encouraging.

I am uncertain about the future of biomedical research. There is serious talk of an additional hundred million dollars a year for cancer and for other things. If that happens, it's likely to have an impact and make the opportunities in chemical biology somewhat better than the opportunities in straight chemistry, but I don't know how much. So then if there's going to be any substantial expansion in opportunities for chemistry, it has to be new outlets, and I have no ideas about that.

The next section, which is somewhat longer, is entitled "Intellectual Future." Prospects are medium, neither terribly bright nor terribly dull. Chemistry is, in my view, a mature science. You have to watch out in evaluating my prejudices. Molecular biologists have a tendency to think that chemistry is basically dead. I remember when Gunther Stent said that organic chemistry was dead in the Golden Age of Science lecture he gave here a few years ago. My colleague, J. D. Roberts, as he was walking out, muttered, "That guy doesn't know a certain part of his anatomy from a hole in the ground." Roberts said that the things that are happening in chemistry now, if you read *Tetrahedron Letters* or *Communications to JACS* or journals like that, are better, there's more new stuff happening, more good stuff happening, than happened 10 years ago. I think he was thinking of things like the Woodward–Hoffman rules and the whole development or understanding of the mechanism of electrocyclic reactions (his understanding, not mine, you understand), the synthesis of novel molecular structures usually strained or otherwise unstable, the development of the chemistry of the interaction of pi-electron systems with transition metals, the developments in nmr, chromatography, X-ray structure analysis, and lots of other wonderful things. These are all great advances, but they don't strike me as conceptual revolutions. I try to think of this in the sense that, supposing I'd retired from the field in 1940 when I got a Ph.D. and come back now, how surprised would I have been, how hard would it have been for me to assimilate these ideas? And most of the new advances, I think, were things we talked about and thought about in a primitive way then.

I'd like to explicitly say that, in my opinion, the purpose of modern science is to be useful. At one time science was a great intellectual liberating force: It liberated us from superstition in the guise of religion, it enlarged our vision of the nature of the physical world and of man, and, then, in the cases of quantum mechanics and relativity, it enlarged our understanding of how we interpret the world. But I think that's practically over. The only part of modern science that can lay a similar claim now is behavioral biology or psychology. We don't understand man as a thinking, feeling being. The rest of natural science will lead to no conceptual revolutions. And a social justification, as distinct from the motivation of the individual scientist discussed by Max Delbrück, will have to be related to its usefulness. In this context, basic research is clearly important, because it is basic. It gives us a versatile base from which to attack and solve a number of problems. I think basic research is going to stay in style. But I think that there will be both intellectual and financial pressure to select those areas of basic research that are likely to be relevant. The practical problems we face concern complex systems. My own feeling is that we're going to decide that the useful kind of basic research, in studying complicated systems, is to study models just one level of complexity down. Research on very simple systems will have a hard time justifying itself because the usefulness of such research for predicting the behavior of complex systems is limited. The problems are just too complicated.

I have a special note here to make the projection that analytical chemistry is going to have a bright future. Even though analytical chemistry as such tends to be in disrepute as a discipline among the more intellectual members of our profession, you can put up a good case for the proposition that a major fraction of progress in chemistry is due to progress in analysis. I am thinking of separation methods based on chromatography and the new wonderful instrumental methods of analysis. I find high-resolution mass spectrometry most spectacular. I can remember when I first started working in gas-phase chemical kinetics around 1946—it was really a speculative morass. People put things in tubes, heated them up, watched the pressure change, and then elaborated mechanisms, but the mechanisms involved reactions that were not, in fact, occurring. And the subject didn't take off until it was possible to analyze reaction products by gas chromatography and mass spectrometry. Similar things have happened in chemical biology—the ability to analyze and sequence nucleic acids and proteins has increased the power of our research a great deal.

The next section is "Other Promising Fields for the Future." I've put down health-related chemistry, and I'll talk about that a little more. And then I put down environmental chemistry in the broad sense of the word. I think this was pretty close to what George was talking about. It involves research that industry and government may be doing in the future, but not quite in the way it's used fashionably now. Man has to learn how to get along on a crowded planet at a reasonable and uniform standard of living without mutagenizing himself into a monster and without fouling his nest. All the style in the developments of industrial chemistry are sure to be conditioned by these long-range considerations and that's going to be a really practical matter.

I suppose I should say a few words about the status of chemical biology. It's not virgin territory any more, but it is a lot more sparsely settled than straight chemistry. There certainly is a lot more room for interesting and unanticipated discoveries. Questions of medical relevance will be asked of the biochemist just as questions of relevance will be asked of the pure chemist. There'll be a lot of room to maneuver and to do interesting things.

This next section is entitled "The Trouble with Chemistry," and it's an expression of some of my beliefs—and you can call them prejudices—about what's wrong with chemistry at the present. I think chemistry is too myopic, too parochial, and too stereotyped. We all have too much of a tendency to do the same thing we learned to do in graduate school. I have the impression, for example, that every reputable chemistry department in the country has inorganic chemists who work on transition-metal-complex ions. I've heard engineers and physicists, but rarely chemists, tell me about the chemistry of semiconductors, about the question of the equilibrium between a boron atom and a boron ion in a diamond lattice. Physicists have a quaint word, positive hole, to take care of this thing. Now I think this is a fascinating field of inorganic chemistry. But, for example, it gets one page in Dickerson, Gray, and Haight (recent freshman chemistry testbook), whereas transition metal complexes get a chapter. Biochemists have done really quite astounding things in developing methods for sequencing proteins and now, even more fantastically, I find, for sequencing ribonucleic acids—with essentially no help from chemists. It's easy for me to take examples from things I sort of naturally hear about in a day's work. There are lots of messy but important biochemical compounds. I heard some guy talking a few months ago about glycoproteins that occur in brain tissue and may conceivably be the key to specificity of neural connections in the brain. But as far as I can see, natural-product chemists won't touch this stuff. They're messier than terpenes and the pigments that occur in flowers and the kinds of things that, it seems to me, natural-product chemists like to work with.

I go to various other, less prestigious departments of chemistry and they're all talking about trying to build a department just like Caltech and Stanford and Berkeley. I think it would be interesting if chemistry departments strove for more individuality and more variety. Why shouldn't a department strive to excel in medicinal chemistry or in the chemistry of the solid state, or in polymers, and yet try to do it in such a way that students were educated in understanding chemical bonding, nonbonding interactions, chemical dynamics, and all those basic topics which enter into each one of these disciplines just as well as into the kind of thing that's done at Caltech? I think that if we did that, we'd have a broader and more diversified and more interesting profession. But these places all hire guys who get their Ph.D.s at Stanford, Caltech, Berkeley, places like that, and unless the people who get their Ph.D.s here are willing to be adventuresome, I don't see much diversification ahead.

Well, I don't know if this last part is striking a fairly pessimistic note. My overall assessment is moderately optimistic. I think chemistry has a reasonably bright future, but the more innovative and adventuresome we are, the brighter the future.

DRICKAMER: I'm somewhat appalled. I felt sure that by now one of these fellows would have gotten lynched and broken up the meeting, so I wasn't really prepared for all this.

DAVIDSON: We reserve lynching for guests.

DRICKAMER: I'm going to start from the viewpoint that a fair number of people feel that there are a fair number of problems with the present situation in chemistry, simply because when things are really booming one doesn't hold meetings on whether chemistry has a future. You're so busy turning out new ideas and new results that you really don't have time. And so I'm trying to see how these problems arise (if there are indeed problems) and possibly some solutions. Now my connections are sort of threefold among physical chemistry, chemical engineering, and solid-state physics. I see certain similarities in these and certain differences. Occasionally I may mention similarities with organic chemistry and show the breadth of my ignorance while I'm doing this.

When I was first aware of what was going on, say the period 1946 to 1950, there was a considerable dissatisfaction among chemical engineers, physical chemists, and I think also organic chemists, vis-à-vis the relative excitement of nuclear physics in the late 1930s and solid-state physics in the late 1940s. Young chemical engineers were talking of the Institute as the packed-tower institute because people tended to devote their time to studying the efficiency of relatively well known separation phenomena. Physical chemists felt that their approach to problems was both unsophisticated and sterile in the sense that thermodynamics had been fairly well milked—that macroscopic measurements of kinetics weren't getting any further. There was also a feeling among organic chemists doing a sort of semiroutine synthesis—which we referred to as sticking another ethyl group in the beta position—that there was a degree of sophistication and a degree of fertility about physics missing in their area.

And in each area we did something about it. In physical chemistry we introduced the ideas of quantum mechanics and group theory from the theoretical standpoint and in spectroscopy the instrumentation of physics, for example microwave, nmr, and esr. In chemical engineering we introduced sophisticated applied mathematics. The notions and the experimental techniques of fluid mechanics to study transport and moving systems got us away from just making thermodynamic measurements. And in organic chemistry, both the instrumentation of physical chemistry and physics and the concepts of physical organic chemistry, that is, chemical dynamics and things of that sort, were introduced. This was indeed very fruitful. We changed both the form and the substance of our approach and there was a burst of output in all these areas which was very significant and still continues to be in many ways.

But in all human endeavors there's a basic conservatism wherein one tends to preserve the form even when some of the substance is gone. This is where I think solid-state physics comes into the picture. We have a successful form which has produced some real substance—something with fertility—and we are reluctant to give up the form. I think that we have tended now to feel that it's more important to be elegant and sophisticated in many ways than it is to be fruitful. In engineering we study relatively simple models for flowing systems; in physical chemistry, relatively simple molecules; in solid-state physics, the alkali halides, and silicon and germanium and things of that sort, and we learned a great deal about these simple systems.

We tend to refine our measurements and refine our calculations without any real hope that a new generalization can ever arise from these studies; that is, you get neater data, more accurate data, more sophisticated study, but what is the possibility that a new generalization will arise? I think very little. I think what we're going to need to do is make some kind of a break—not everybody, of course. You understand that what I'm saying here is a caricature, but I hope that as in any good caricature, there are some recognizable features.

I think that we really need to turn in some different directions and this is in some way related I think to the latter part of Norm Davidson's talk; that is, people have to be willing to do a little more exploratory work. But it is difficult to open up new fields. Even though sophisticated techniques may be used, the treatment may have to be relatively unsophisticated because it's a really new idea. I think of Mott and Jones. This is a book on the structure of solids, really the structure of metals, printed in 1936. I was talking to Mott two or three years ago and he said, "Of course you understand that all that's wrong." It was unsophisticated, but it was probably the most seminal book ever written on an area of that kind, because it contained a lot of ideas that could be tested and refined. I think we have to break into new areas with seminal treatments of this kind. They may be relatively unsophisticated, but I think we will have to become interested and excited about partial solutions to large problems rather than complete solutions to very small problems. We'll have to worry about interacting with other fields even when it's not possible in a very sophisticated way. Much of geochemistry, for example, looks to be kind of unsophisticated and crude but yet one might make a real breakthrough, a real understanding of something by attacking these silicates in some complex way. You won't be able to make the measurements that you can on a simple pure single crystal of NaCl, and, for what measurements you can make, the interpretations may be somewhat broad and a little bit obscured. But you might really introduce some new ideas, and extend where we're going.

I think that relevance is a very dangerous term. I come from an engineering education and the engineering education of 30 years ago was relevant. We studied know-how, which was obsolete before we got out of school (and it had to be unless the field was dead), but I think that there was no harm in studying specific systems of real use, systems in which you could do something interesting and exciting. I can recall a time 20 years ago when a man told me that the thing that made him proud to be in his branch of chemistry was that there was no possible way of applying it. I think that kind of attitude was nonsense then and is nonsense today. Some of the most exciting chemistry or physics of, say, silicon or germanium came about because it was *important* to understand their properties—and it was darn good science. In the case of the doping of crystals it was darn good chemistry but we couldn't find any chemists to do it, so it had to be done by a physicist. Applied work, for example, nowadays work on amorphous materials, is an area where people could break in.

Finally I should like to reemphasize that there are problems in breaking into a new field, there are problems in being exploratory. I realize that you're in a position where engineers say, "Well, you might have been a pretty good engineer if you ever did any"; on the other hand, chemists will say, "That's pretty interesting stuff, too bad it's not chemistry," and physicists will say, "Well, considering you're not a physicist, it isn't as bad as it might be"; etc. This isn't an easy thing to do. To ask young people to do it and to stick their necks out I think is asking a considerable bit. There are practical difficulties, like getting support and interesting graduate students. But even more there are important psychological difficulties. Man is a social animal and it's a kind of comforting thing to be able to go to a meeting and find a half a dozen other people doing very nearly the same thing. You can talk and it's exciting. There's competition but there's also a feeling of companionship out of this. And when you're doing things that aren't quite like what other people are doing, they say, "Well, gee, that's fine stuff. By the way, did you hear about what I am doing. . . ?" I think that if we are going to try to encourage young people to do this, it behooves us who are perhaps somewhat established to move out and be somewhat exploratory, not in deference to the young people, but for our own self-respect; I think that perhaps we ought to start whatever revolution we're going to start with people our age doing the revolting and moving out.

PINGS: I promised the panelists, who have prepared remarks, that they could have first crack at each other, so I'll see if they have any pent-up feelings that they wish to vent right now. George, do you have anything to say in reply—not on your speech, please—anything to reply to these other two presentations?

HAMMOND: Yes. Let me say something in response. I've been sitting here in the middle, and . . . hell, I really am in the middle. Because when I talk about where chemistry is going, I talk about outlets into other fields, and the two fields I always pick are biological chemistry, which is well established, and engineering science, which I think is becoming established. On my left I have a man who clearly has flowed through the breach in the wall and is over there in this less populated and very interesting area of biological chemistry. And on my right there's Harry, who a long time ago discovered the other thing that people are just beginning to discover. I guess I'm just a poor cat who's stuck back in the middle, which is not the sort of image I like to have of myself. I do not think that the middle is totally dead. The fact of the matter is that we guys in the middle probably do one hell of a good job—as good a job as anybody really cares about or is going to learn a lot from—in calculating the ionization energy of benzene. No doubt about it. And so that is probably pretty dead. As dead as Norman and Harry make it sound. But I don't think either of these guys can do such a good job with the boiling point of benzene. And that's neither engineering nor biochemistry, its chemistry.

DAVIDSON: I was going to ask what the boiling point of benzene is.

HAMMOND: 84°?

DAVIDSON: 80°? 78°?

HAMMOND: Well. *I* haven't boiled it recently. Maybe it's changed in the meantime.

DRICKAMER: As an organic chemist I think there was probably something in your benzene.

DAVIDSON: I have another question, but I think I'd rather participate in this discussion. I suspect that there are some problems, like the statistical mechanics of liquids, that are just not going to be solved theoretically. I think that we're going to end up by taking the attitude that we can measure the boiling point of benzene with a flask and a thermometer, and calculating it is just not going to be popular.

HAMMOND: There was a time when anyone would have said that about the ionization potential.

DAVIDSON: OK, but I said that right now about the boiling point of benzene. I may be wrong.

PINGS: Yes, but you certainly hope that if you did do it with a flask and a thermometer, that then when you stuck the ethyl group in the beta position, you wouldn't have to repeat it for the new substance. There is some building you can do.

HAMMOND: In fact, Wilse Robinson may have the boiling point of benzene while you're still around to admire it. I mean benzene isn't argon, but hell. . . .

DAVIDSON: Well, the point is the following: Unless after Wilse gets done with benzene he really *can* do ethylbenzene and 3-ethylnitrobenzene. . . .

ROBINSON (from the audience): Why are you picking on me, Norman?

DAVIDSON: George Hammond picked on you, I didn't. Well, I don't *think* I'm picking on you.

HAMMOND: I didn't pick on him, I pinned my faith on him.

DAVIDSON: I'm trying to seriously raise the question of whether it is really valuable to calculate the properties of certain simple systems when we know in a qualitative sense what's involved in the theory and it's dubious whether the quantitative success of the theory will ever be sufficient to enable us to figure out things that we couldn't just as easily measure.

HAMMOND: In my opinion, yes. And I'll tell you why. I think that behind all this the urge for all this is not to know the boiling point of benzene—because even if I forget it I can look it up—but it's because coming out of this, the second-generation or third-generation development will, I think, be enormously fruitful inspiration for doing exactly the sort of thing that Harry cited as being extremely important—and that is, understanding the properties and behavior of amorphous systems in general.

DAVIDSON: That kind of theory I'm in favor of.

PINGS: Good. We agree on something.

DAVIDSON: Listen. I thought we agreed on a lot. I thought we were really saying very similar things.

PINGS: Yes. As a matter of fact, I'm beginning to despair right now, because we're going to lag. Harry, what do you have to say about all this?

DRICKAMER: Well, I think it's very easy to sit up here and lecture people on where we ought to go, but I've been trying to remember why it is that people stick so much to the form. I guess it's simply because they know they can accomplish something. They know they can do a reasonable job with a student in a reasonable time, and the real question is how practical is this exploratory work as a means of getting people degrees? That's a very difficult problem.

And that leads me to another point, which is somewhat aside from what we made here, but it's a point related to your statistics and numbers up there. I think that one of the problems we face in universities is some decoupling between the natural desire of the faculty to do research and the available jobs for graduate students.

I think if you really came down to it nationwide, I don't know about Caltech, but the number of students in graduate school depends only on two factors: the amount of money you've got to support them, and the amount of people that the faculty want working with them. It's in no sense even remotely correlated to the possibilities of them getting jobs in the future, in the long run. In the first place one doesn't know about that, and in the second place, in an expanding economy we haven't had to worry about that. There have always been jobs of some kind and they moved into these jobs. But I cannot see a fastly expanding job market taking care of the number of students we're going to turn out. I think there is a possible solution here that may be helpful to the students, especially in the sense that with a more limited output there may be more opportunities. The people at places like Bell Labs have done it very well, and that's introducing a much larger flavor of technicians to a university. I think that biologists also have done this better than we have. In other words, a typical man, instead of having, say, six graduate students, as he might in an area of physical chemistry, would have three graduate students and a technician. I arrived at that number not because he's going to get the same amount of research done, but because it's going to cost about the same amount of money. There's no use proposing solutions that have no chance of going through, and any solution that involves a heck of a lot more money isn't going to go through at all. I think, however, that he could accomplish a good deal of research. This would solve a problem in the four-year schools, where people are pushing to get graduate work, really not because a lot more graduate students are needed, but because they really want graduate students to work with them. In the best of all possible worlds they have graduate students to work with but in the second-best of all possible worlds, perhaps two faculty at Oberlin could share a technician. They could then accomplish some research, get something done, and still remain in their teaching function. I think the disadvantages to this system are smaller than the vast expansion of the offering of the Ph.D. degree we've seen in the past two decades. There are far too many places offering the Ph.D. A man can shop around at almost any intellectual level and find a place where he can get it.

I just bring this up as maybe sort of a bookkeeping detail compared with the big picture we're talking about, but I think it would be a serious detail in the life of students if the number of people were limited by the fact that people are only encouraged to go on if they have a particular vocation for it.

PINGS: I'd like to open this now for comments or questions from the audience. If you wish you may address your questions to specific individuals.

ARON KUPPERMANN (from the audience): . . . If we work out Norm Davidson's premise that in the future problems at the level of scientific complexity that will be tackled most, astronomy is the one immediately below the level of relevance, being I guess the . . .

DAVIDSON: . . . the level of interest . . .

KUPPERMANN: . . . being that you're just off by one order of magnitude, you'd have a better chance of jumping the gap than if you're several orders away. That may be so for a substantial fraction of chemistry but I feel that it should not and will not be so for an excessive amount of it. The reason is that this depends on one man's opinion of where past breakthroughs and understandings have really occurred. If you ask yourself what can be simpler than a hydrogen atom in chemistry, you'd have a hard time finding something. Nevertheless, it was the study of the hydrogen atom by quantum mechanics that had a tremendous impact on all of chemistry, and it's not likely in the future that we'll have that kind of breakthrough again. But it's quite conceivable that the understanding of very simple systems in sufficient detail will indeed do jumps in orders of magnitude above its standing in other areas of chemistry; for example, if one understands in a certain level of detail the energy management of molecules, how molecules manipulate energy during chemical reaction, etc., it's quite conceivable that one can have in the future a whole new type of energy source, chemical energy source, an energy-storage type of mechanism evolved, and it might not be the one very closely related to the problem of how to store energy chemically. I think that one should be a little careful about sticking too close to the immediate relevance, but that big jumps are possible and likely.

DAVIDSON: Point one: I absolutely agree with you. Everything ever discovered about the hydrogen atom has been relevant, in the sense that it has enlarged our understanding of a large number of physical systems. I may be myopic, but I'm not equally convinced that everything that is discovered about the reaction $H + Cl$ or $H + H_2$ is going to enlarge our understanding of more complex chemical dynamic systems. That's an intuition.

HAMMOND: I'd like to comment on the same thing because I think that there's an implication in what both Aron and Norman said which is, unfortunately, extreme. Now I agree with Aron, in that I think that somewhere there are more breakthroughs to come from working with simple systems, and the system he cited is a good candidate. Although you don't know where a breakthrough is going to come until it comes, that's what a breakthrough is all about. On the other hand, I also know very well that breakthroughs do not, have not, come uniquely from the study of small, simple systems. You only have to think back and realize that Sadi Carnot got one hell of a lot from screwing around with steam engines. He really did. But I'm optimistic. I think that breakthroughs of some kind are likely to come from all kinds of work, not uniquely in complex, not uniquely in small.

DAVIDSON: Neil, I'd like to be sure not to be misunderstood. And I guess what I'm trying to communicate could be said by saying that if I were, for example, the big cheese in the NSF, like some of my friends almost became, I would believe in supporting research across the board, including the study of simple systems, but in terms of the emphasis and relative distribution of support, things would be shaded in accordance with the kind of view that I expressed.

HAMMOND: You know, I would have agreed with you.

STEN SAMSON: . . . In many cases from a very complicated system— I'm now thinking about structures—you obtain a vast number and variety of information that you never obtain from a simple system. I think we can obtain information from a complicated system that will shed significant light on simple systems. Phenomenological theories, I think, are the ones that might be studied, and my feeling is that phenomenological theories will be very, very useful, particularly in solid-state physics. As far as structures are concerned, I think complicated systems are more useful to study than the simple ones.

PINGS: Again it's a question of balance, isn't it? And one thing I think we can say for sure is that no one has thought out that question of balance—we sort of evolve into it. But I think even the national agencies in the allocation of resources have not necessarily done this. Of course, it cannot be done perfectly, but I don't think it's ever been done to a first approximation.

DRICKAMER: Well, I don't think anyone is really arguing that we should give up simple systems, or give up complicated systems. I guess my point was that I think that the balance, if I look over physics and physical chemistry, is too far in the direction of being very sophisticated about relatively simple systems. I'm thinking of solid-state physics, which I know more about than I do any of these other aspects. And I see an awful lot of physicists making a very large number of precise measurements, but they don't seem to even visualize where this is going, except that now you can measure and predict very accurately the quadrupole splitting on a given ion in a given crystal but then when you ask what generalizations arise from it they say, "Well, of course in another crystal the symmetry's going to be different and you have to start all over. But it makes another thesis."

HAMMOND: I want to comment on what was said in this matter of balance, and I don't think the important thing really is balance between working on complicated and working on simple, because things can happen anywhere. But I think that you do have some grounds of predicting the likelihood, in a rough way, that a particular kind of work is likely to lead to a breakthrough. It's very much what Harry Drickamer said. If this work is very much like other work which has been done and done a number of times, chances are that it isn't going to have that quality. What makes the kind of structural work done by Sten Samson really fine is not that his metal systems are complicated, which they are, or if they were simple, that they were simple, but the fact that they are damned different from systems that other people have done.

DRICKAMER: That's a good point. Very good point.

QUESTION: We have heard a number of comments about success of continual reappraisal, taking off in new directions. I get the feeling that this has a real need; I also get the feeling that the only help you can offer is moral exhortation.

DRICKAMER: My point was that I think that those of us who are leading the cheering ought to do it and then maybe by example other people would, rather than tell the young people, "Well, take over." Of course, you've got to have enough juice left to do it, and we may or may not have, but I think that's up to us to demonstrate.

HAMMOND: My response to that is that this moral exhortation sounds as though it's all sermonettes delivered to other people. Part of it is me talking to myself, and I don't respond as fast as I would like, but in some ways I respond.

QUESTION: One thing in particular brought to mind when Dr. Drickamer talked about the difficulty with people going into a new area: Getting money and a position are very hard when you start in something new.

DRICKAMER: I still think that the psychological problem is tougher, though, than the practical ones.

HAMMOND: I think that the psychological problem is becoming attenuated. Because a few years ago if you tried to do something quite new, people would really cut you off. But now the value system has changed a little bit and two things have happened. One, something that is quite new is looked on a little bit more carefully and sympathetically, because that's now the "in" thing to do, some people do it; and the other thing is that it's getting god-damned unpopular to do the old stuff, because some of that's going to be cut off simply because it's faddish to cut off the old. And so it will become easy.

QUESTION: I feel that chemists should do a lot more synthesis of things for a specific purpose.

HAMMOND: I agree. I think that the historical origin of natural-product synthetic chemistry, which is by all odds a most sophisticated field, is very clearly exactly that: produce a material, a new material, to produce a property; the properties people were after were physiological properties. That mission is partly forgotten now, but that's where it came from. And I think other, similar fields of synthesis probably can develop from a similar basis. Define a property, get a model, no matter how freaky, for relating that property to structure, make the structure, and see how it goes.

QUESTION: I think two factors prohibit people from breaking into new fields and being exploratory. One is simply the old publish-or-perish syndrome, which tends to place too much emphasis on numbers of papers published, since there are more people with tenure than there are grants from the granting agencies. Another factor, I think, is that our whole education system, going back into kindergarten, still rewards people for getting the right answers. We don't encourage them to learn and explore.

HAMMOND: Yes. The probability of your looking like a total ass if you do something really new is pretty high.

DRICKAMER: On the other hand, it's fairly probable that if it's new enough, it'll be quite a few years before people find that out. I've been living that way for 20 years.

PINGS: I have a question to ask Norman Davidson with regard to your comment that there is an unfortunate situation where there are too many departments that look at Caltech and Harvard and try to model themselves after this standard image. . . .

DRICKAMER: None of you people say Illinois, dammit.

PINGS: . . . how do you reconcile this to the fact that you belong to the ACS, which makes a fetish of sending people around the country to find out what Caltech, Illinois, and Harvard are doing, and then going out into the bushes and telling other departments, "You must do it this way or we'll take your accreditation away"?

HAMMOND: That's a slander.

PINGS: Are you suggesting that it's not true?

HAMMOND: Yes.

DAVIDSON: This is really George's area of competence. He *is* a member of the Western College Accreditation Board.

HAMMOND: No I *was* a member of the Committee for six years. And I must say that the things that have been written in our pamphlet probably are never read. I know, because I wrote some of them. And the fact of the matter is that that Committee has evolved a very good attitude, I think, toward experimentation and really wants to know what people are doing that's new, rather than wanting to know what they're doing that's just like Caltech and Illinois. The hell of it is that the response of people is that these are dictates, no matter how often you write down that these are broad outlines and that we recognize and encourage extreme deviation from it. Nobody'll read that. It's a problem. I mean if you disband the Committee there won't be that whipping boy to hang your conservatism on. But you'd find one.

PINGS: O.K. Sorry. I'm stupid, not slanderous.

HAMMOND: Have you read it?

PINGS: No. I don't have time to read that. But I don't want this to end either with a lynching or an accusation of slander, so I will tolerate one more question or comment from the audience.

J. D. ROBERTS (from audience): I think one problem with professional societies, at least the chemical ones, is that some of them want to do what the AMA is doing and some of them want to foster chemistry as an industrial complex kind of thing, generally. But there's very little emphasis in any of them on the way chemistry ought to be used. The developments of society to chemistry is having a large effect on society, but a study of this kind of thing isn't being approached, as far as I can see, by the ACS, and I don't see much hope that it will be. The National Academy's doing a little bit, but not very much.

HAMMOND: Can I respond to that, because I'm now on *that* committee?

PINGS: We're just getting in deeper, Jack.

HAMMOND: The fact of the matter is that I really entirely agree with Jack, and the ACS Committee on Chemistry in Public Affairs is trying—this is run by Frank Long, and Frank is Frank, and you know how he feels about these matters—trying very hard to activate something which may be of some significance. It *is* difficult, because of the character of the society, because of the character of chemists; and because of the fact that it hasn't been done, we have to fool around doing a lot of thinking about what's an effective style, and simply emoting is not good. One of the things which has happened, and is fairly significant, again this is Long, and that's the ACS Monograph on Chemistry and Environment, which actually is generally referred to as the best documentary on environmental problems that exists in any technological way. This is just a tiny beginning. There's another thing that the ACS does, which you didn't mention, and that's try to preserve the rites of the system in much the same way that the Pope does for his outfit.

PINGS: Does the panel have any concluding remarks? Harry? Norman? George? Anything further you want to add?

HAMMOND: I don't dare add anything.